ANIMAL BEHAVIOR:
THEORY
AND RESEARCH

BASIC CONCEPTS IN PSYCHOLOGY SERIES

Edward L. Walker, Editor

GENERAL

PSYCHOLOGY AS A NATURAL AND SOCIAL SCIENCE	Edward L. Walker
TEACHING THE BEGINNING COURSE IN PSYCHOLOGY	Edward L. Walker and Wilbert J. McKeachie
A LABORATORY MANUAL FOR THE CONTROL AND ANALYSIS OF BEHAVIOR	Harlan L. Lane and Daryl J. Bem
QUANTIFICATION IN PSYCHOLOGY	William L. Hays
BASIC STATISTICS	William L. Hays

PSYCHOLOGY: A NATURAL SCIENCE

NEUROPSYCHOLOGY: THE STUDY OF BRAIN AND BEHAVIOR	Charles M. Butter
SENSORY PROCESSES	Mathew Alpern, Merle Lawrence, and David Wolsk
PERCEPTION	Daniel J. Weintraub and Edward L. Walker
PERCEPTUAL DEMONSTRATION KIT	Daniel J. Weintraub and Edward L. Walker
HUMAN PERFORMANCE	Paul M. Fitts and Michael I. Posner
CONDITIONING AND INSTRUMENTAL LEARNING	Edward L. Walker
COMPARATIVE PSYCHOLOGY	Richard A. Maier and Barbara M. Maier
ANIMAL BEHAVIOR: THEORY AND RESEARCH	F. Joseph Mortenson

PSYCHOLOGY: A SOCIAL SCIENCE

MOTIVATION: A STUDY OF ACTION	David Birch and Joseph Veroff
PSYCHODYNAMICS: THE SCIENCE OF UNCONSCIOUS MENTAL FORCES	Gerald S. Blum
ASSESSMENT OF HUMAN CHARACTERISTICS	E. Lowell Kelly
COGNITIVE PROCESSES	Melvin Manis
SOCIAL PSYCHOLOGY: AN EXPERIMENTAL APPROACH	Robert B. Zajonc
NON-FREUDIAN PERSONALITY THEORIES	P. James Geiwitz
BELIEFS, ATTITUDES, AND HUMAN AFFAIRS	Daryl J. Bem
CLINICAL PSYCHOLOGY: AN EMPIRICAL APPROACH	Erasmus L. Hoch
ABNORMAL PSYCHOLOGY	James Neal Butcher

ANIMAL BEHAVIOR: THEORY AND RESEARCH

F. JOSEPH MORTENSON
Mount St. Vincent University

BROOKS/COLE PUBLISHING COMPANY
Monterey, California

A Division of Wadsworth Publishing Company, Inc.

For my mother and father

ISBN: 0–8185–0147–2
L.C. Catalog Card No.: 74–30500
Printed in the United States of America

10 9 8 7 6 5 4 3 2 1

Production Editor: *Lyle York*
Interior Design: *Linda Marcetti*
Cover Design: *John Edeen*
Illustrations: *John Foster*
Typesetting: *Datagraphics Press, Inc., Phoenix, Arizona*
Printing & Binding: *R. R. Donnelly & Sons, Inc., Crawfordsville, Indiana*

SERIES FOREWORD

Basic Concepts in Psychology was conceived as a series of brief paperback volumes constituting a beginning textbook in psychology. Several unique advantages arise from publishing individual chapters as separate volumes rather than under a single cover. Each book or chapter can be written by an author identified with the subject matter of the area. New chapters can be added, individual chapters can be revised independently, and, possibly, competitive chapters can be provided for controversial areas. Finally, to a degree, an instructor of the beginning course in psychology can choose a particular set of chapters to meet the needs of his students.

Probably the most important impetus for the series came from the fact that a suitable textbook did not exist for the beginning courses in psychology at the University of Michigan—Psychology 100 (Psychology as a Natural Science) and Psychology 101 (Psychology as a Social Science). In addition, no laboratory manual treated both the natural science and social science problems encountered in the first laboratory course, Psychology 110.

For practical rather than ideological reasons most of the original complement of authors came from the staff of the University of Michigan. As the series has developed, authors have been selected from other institutions in an effort to assure national representation and a broad perspective in contemporary psychology.

Each author in the Basic Concepts in Psychology Series has considerable freedom. He has been charged to devote approximately half of his resources to elementary concepts and half to topics of special interest and emphasis. In this way, each volume will reflect the personality and viewpoint of the author while presenting the subject matter usually found in a chapter of an elementary textbook.

ACKNOWLEDGMENTS

Thanks must be given to all those who commented on the manuscript of *Animal Behavior: Theory and Research.* Of special value were the thoughtful suggestions of the late Terry Anders of Dalhousie University, Donald Dewsbury of the University of Florida, Michael Fox of Washington University, St. Louis, Nancy Innis of the University of Western Ontario, Nicholas Mackintosh of Sussex University, Ian McLaren of Dalhousie University, Horst Schwassmann of the University of Florida, Stephen Suomi of the University of Wisconsin, William Timberlake of Indiana University, and Brooks/Cole's consulting editor, Edward L. Walker. I would also like to express appreciation to Marie Campbell, Nancy Kinsman, and the other secretaries at the Department of Psychology of Dalhousie University; my original draft often proved a test of secretarial skills.

F. Joseph Mortenson

INTRODUCTION

In the laboratories of colleges and universities, academics make careers out of the study of the white rat. In quiet museums, scholars ponder the bones of extinct primates in an attempt to reconstruct the natural history of these animals. In the field, scientists with binoculars describe the territories held by birds. All these people—and many others—are students of animal behavior. Their backgrounds vary: their scientific training may have been in psychology, zoology, anthropology, or even in physiology or wildlife management. Their research specializations are diverse; there is frequently little overlap in the primary interests of different animal behaviorists.

This book is an introduction to the multifaceted science of animal behavior. The book will give the reader an appreciation for the diversity of both backgrounds and interests among students in the field. Part I considers the development of three contemporary theoretical schools. Students trained in these schools have characteristic and often contrasting orientations to animal behavior. A grasp of these students' backgrounds helps the reader to understand the value of their contributions to our knowledge of animal behavior. The final chapter in Part I deals with some points of agreement among contemporary theorists and with the ensuing potential for a more unified approach to animal behavior. In Part II, five research areas are reviewed in some depth. The areas chosen represent the kind of problems that intrigue animal behaviorists and illustrate exciting advances that have been made in the study of animal behavior during the last two decades. The last chapter in Part II draws on material introduced at different points in the book in its examination of the evolution and causation of primate behavior, including that of humans.

CONTENTS

THE EVOLUTION OF THREE CONTEMPORARY APPROACHES TO ANIMAL BEHAVIOR

PART 1

Part 1 begins with a brief history of the study of animal behavior. First we examine the ways in which many of the first animal behaviorists attempted to describe the minds of animals. Then we trace the history of three contemporary schools that replaced the study of animal mind. In the United States, the behavioristic movement began as a protest against mentalistic animal psychology. In Russia, Pavlov founded the psychophysiological approach. In Europe, the science of ethology developed when young zoologists began to study behavior in natural settings. In the final chapter of Part 1, we consider some grounds for rapprochement among the three contemporary viewpoints.

EARLY HISTORY 1

The study of animal behavior is in many ways a new science: it is only in this century that fully developed theories of animal behavior have proliferated, and in the last few decades there has been a dramatic increase in the quality and quantity of research into animal behavior.

Although the study of animal behavior is a new science, it is in other ways an ancient art. Since long before the growth of the Western scientific tradition, humans have been keen students of animal behavior. Their knowledge has given them an immediate advantage in hunting and in managing domesticated animals. Their theories about animals, however, have often revealed more about human behavior than about nonhuman behavior. For example, in various human societies, animals were assumed to possess beneficial powers and to be able to grant requests to human petitioners; their behavior might forecast future events; they were often considered to be ancestral to humans and therefore were regarded as protecting spirits. They were sometimes even deified. These beliefs about animals have reflected human fears and needs.

To this day, some prescientific interpretations of animal behavior persist in Western European culture. For example, one important set of concepts springs from the dichotomy that often has been assumed to exist between man and beast (see Beach, 1955). From the time of the Greek philosophers, humans have been frequently considered godlike beings: they possess immortal souls and are capable of reasoning. Animals, on the other hand, have no souls; their behavior is determined by instinct. This dichotomous conception lingers in various areas of Western religious, philosophic, and scientific thought as well as in many laymen's views of animal behavior.

THE SCIENCE OF ANIMAL BEHAVIOR

One cannot assign a precise date to the beginning of the science of animal behavior. Objective reports on animal behavior have appeared throughout recorded history. For instance, extensive empirical observations may be found in Aristotle's *Historia Animalium* (see Warden, 1927). Crude but reasonable theories have also been with us since ancient times. For example, the great Roman naturalist Pliny believed that the function of territoriality in eagles was to secure access to an adequate food supply (Howard, 1920).

For a long time, however, there was no systematic development of a science of animal behavior. Objective observations and brief theoretical statements occurred in isolation; no progress was made beyond them. Indeed, some of these early reports and theoretical notions have only recently been unearthed.

CHARLES DARWIN

It was with Charles Darwin (Figure 1.1) that the science of animal behavior really began its development. Darwin was, of course, the great expositor of the doctrine of evolution. Darwin (1871) believed that the mind, as well as the body, evolved, and that human and animal minds were different in degree rather than in kind. Humans shared even with the "lower" animals the basic mental phenomena of pleasure, pain, happiness, misery, terror, suspicion, rage, fear, maternal affection, wonder, attention, and reason. In addition, to varying degrees, humans shared with "higher" animals such qualities as jealousy, love, pride, shame, modesty, magnanimity, curiosity, and imitation. Darwin even went so far as to argue that birds have a sense of appreciation for beauty superior to that of "savages." Darwin's conception of a mental con-

Figure 1.1

Charles Darwin. From Darwin, 1891.

tinuum between humans and other animals stood in sharp contrast to the traditional view that there was a dichotomy between them.

Darwin had a special interest in the expressive behavior that accompanied mental states. In his book *The Expression of the Emotions in Man and Animals* (1872), Darwin presented three principles that he believed described the origin of expressive movements. According to the first principle, the principle of serviceable associated habits (see Figure 1.2), "movements which are serviceable in gratifying some desire, or in relieving some sensation, if often repeated, become so habitual that they are performed, whether or not of any service, whenever the same desire of sensations is felt, even in a very weak degree" (p. 347). These expressive movements could be inherited. The second principle, the principle of antithesis (see Figure 1.3), was that "if certain actions have been regularly performed, in accordance with [the] first principle, under a certain frame of mind, there will be a strong and involuntary tendency to the performance of directly opposite actions, whether or not these are of any use, under the excitement of an opposite frame of mind" (pp. 347–348). The third principle was that the animal's excited

Figure 1.2

A dog approaching another dog or a man "in a hostile frame of mind." According to the principle of serviceable associated habits, the dog should show movements that had been of service in previous conflicts. From Darwin, 1872.

Figure 1.3

The same dog in an affectionate state of mind. An illustration of the principle of antithesis. The movements, although not of "direct service" to the animal, are the antithesis to those that accompany a hostile frame of mind. From Darwin, 1872.

nervous system acted directly on the existing nervous connections, including those established by habit. This direct action of the nervous system took place independently of the animal's will.

According to Darwin, in both humans and the lower animals, the chief expressive movements were inherited. The evidence cited for this theory in humans was that these expressions were common to young children, to persons born blind, and to different human cultures. However, some seemingly innate gestures, such as the joining of the uplifted hands in prayer, were learned by the individual in his lifetime.

GEORGE JOHN ROMANES

George John Romanes (Figure 1.4) was Darwin's immediate intellectual successor in the study of the animal mind. Romanes was born in Kingston, Ontario, and moved to England as a child; he traveled extensively as a youth and had relatively little formal education before entering Cambridge (E. Romanes, 1896). He was later befriended by Charles Darwin and became concerned with the evolution of the mind, writing three influential books, *Animal Intelligence* (1882), *Mental*

Figure 1.4

George John Romanes. From E. Romanes, 1896.

Evolution in Animals (1885), and *Mental Evolution in Man* (1888). He died in 1894, before he could complete preliminary work for a book on religion.

Romanes (1885) argued that the only thoughts and feelings that one could really know were one's own. However, one could infer the mental activities of other people and of other animals. If our behavior resembled that shown by another organism, we could infer that a mental state that is like our own existed in that organism. As Romanes put it:

All our knowledge of mental activities other than our own reality consists of an inferential interpretation of bodily activities—this interpretation being founded on our subjective knowledge of our own mental activities. By inference we project, as it were, the known patterns of our own mental chromograph on what is to us the otherwise blank screen of another mind; and our only knowledge of the processes there taking place is really due to such a projection of our own subjectively [1885, p. 16].

This form of inference was called the *ejective method,* and the mind or mental process inferred was called an *eject.*

Romanes used the ejective method to infer the evolution of the mind. To illustrate Romanes' conclusions, let's consider the order of appearance of the emotions during evolution. The annelids (worms) and the larvae of insects were the lowest animals to show surprise and fear. Sexual emotions appeared in the mollusks (shellfish). The insects and spiders exhibited parental affection, social feelings, sexual selectivity, pugnacity, industry, and curiosity. Fish were the first group to display jealousy, anger, and play. The social insects were the lowest animals to experience sympathy; the reptiles showed affection. The birds introduced emulation, pride, resentment, aesthetic love of ornament, and terror. The more intelligent carnivores, rodents, and ruminants showed grief, hate, cruelty, and benevolence. Monkeys, cats, and elephants evinced vengeance and rage. The anthropoid apes and dogs added shame, remorse, deceitfulness, and a sense of the ludicrous to the list of emotions shared by humans and nonhumans.

If one grants the validity of the ejective method and does not question Romanes' evidence, one might be compelled to take Romanes' inferences seriously. But the ejective method has a weakness, which Romanes himself acknowledged: among very dissimilar organisms, similarities in behavior may not indicate parallel mental experiences. Other weaknesses in Romanes' approach were recognized by C. Lloyd Morgan, a prominent student of animal behavior who began to publish around the time of Romanes' death.

C. LLOYD MORGAN

C. Lloyd Morgan (Figure 1.5) was taking a degree in mining and metallurgy at the Royal School of Mines (Morgan, 1932) when he met Thomas Huxley at an annual student-staff dinner. Morgan expressed appreciation for Huxley's writings and lamented his own ignorance of biology. At the end of the evening, Huxley suggested that Morgan put in a year's study under his supervision. Morgan accepted his offer and afterward secured a teaching position at a small South African college. There he read Romanes but was put off by his use of anecdotal evidence as a basis for comparative psychology: "Most of the stories were merely casual records, supplemented by amateurish opinions of passing observers whose psychological training was well-nigh negligible" (1932, p. 247).

Morgan returned to England to teach at University College Bristol. At first he wrote on biology and geology, but his interest soon turned to mental evolution. His book *Animal Life and Intelligence* appeared in 1891. Unsatisfied with the existing evidence on the distinction between instinct and intelligence, Morgan began to conduct what we would describe today as informal experiments. He observed dogs, incubator-hatched birds of various species, and other animals. Like Romanes, his aim then as well as later was to "get at the mind of the chick

Figure 1.5

C. Lloyd Morgan. From Murchison, C., *A History of Psychology in Autobiography,* Clark University Press, 1932. Reprinted by permission.

or the dog ... through the close observation of behaviour." But he recognized the difficulties:

The plain tale of behaviour, as we observe and describe it, yields only, as I have put it, body-story and not mind-story. Mind-story is always "imputed" insofar as one can put oneself in the place of another. And this "imputation" ... must always be hazardous [1932, p. 249].

Morgan's *Introduction to Comparative Psychology* was published in 1894. In this book, he expressed his caution in the interpretation of animal behavior with his famous canon:

In no case may we interpret an action as the outcome of an exercise of a higher psychical faculty, if it can be interpreted as the outcome of the exercise of one which stands lower in the psychological scale [p. 53].

He also believed that "association founded on sense-experience" could account for much of the intelligence seen in animals, and he thought that the small number of instances that implied that animals possessed higher faculties might eventually be explained by this principle of association.

Morgan continued to publish influential books; however, in Russia, America, and continental Europe, new and radically different approaches to animal behavior had begun to evolve. Morgan's research had anticipated many of the notions that would surface in these new movements. Nonetheless, the new schools went their own ways; and, although the students in the Darwin-Romanes-Morgan tradition of the study of the animal mind were active up to the 1930s, today their works lie largely unread and uncited.

The next three chapters will consider the evolution of three of the new schools of animal behavior. The first, which originated in nineteenth-century Russia, is known as the study of higher nervous activity. The second, which began around the turn of the century, may be called American animal psychology. The third was foreshadowed in the works of two American zoologists but found its impetus in the writings of the Austrian Konrad Lorenz; it emerged following World War II as the classical school of ethology. The three schools are prominent today and have shaped the basic orientations of many contemporary animal behaviorists.

IVAN MIKHAILOVICH SECHENOV

The first objective approach to the study of behavior was the product of imperial Russia (see Koshtoyants, not dated). Its originator, Ivan Mikhailovich Sechenov (Figure 2.1), was a graduate of the Military Engineering School and of the University of Moscow in medicine. After receiving his degree at Moscow, Sechenov spent three and one-half years abroad working in the laboratories of the famous physiologists Du Bois-Reymond, Ludwig, and Helmholtz. At this time, exciting advances were being made in the understanding of physiological processes such as circulation and digestion. Sechenov came to believe that the methods of natural science would also work in his field of interest, mental or psychical activity.

Figure 2.1

Ivan Mikhailovich Sechenov. From Sechenov, I. M.,
Selected Physiological and Psychological Works. Reprinted by permission of Progress Publishers.

In the late 1850s and early 1860s, Sechenov refined and elaborated this radical new position on the study of mental activity. He finally published his views in 1863 as *Reflexes of the Brain* only after the censor had rejected the original title and conclusion and had refused to allow Sechenov to publish it in the journal he had chosen. In *Reflexes of the Brain,* Sechenov argued that the objective methods of natural science ought to be applied to the study of mental processes, and that mental processes originate in reflexes and are initiated and sustained by external stimulation. Sechenov subsequently became embroiled in a long dispute with the psychologist Kavelin over the principles expressed in *Reflexes of the Brain.* Sechenov responded to Kavelin's criticism with articles, one of which was entitled "Who Is to Elaborate the Problem of Psychology and How," in which he asserted that it was the physiologist who ought to study behavior, and that psychology ought to replace its speculations and metaphysics with a physiological approach to the analysis of mental phenomena.

Sechenov's suggestions awaited the arrival of I. P. Pavlov for their fruition.

IVAN PETROVICH PAVLOV

Ivan Petrovich Pavlov (Figure 2.2), the son of a village priest, was born in 1849. Young Vanya played hard as a child and went to the church school. From there, he was sent to a theological seminary, but he left without finishing to go to the University of St. Petersburg. At the university, Pavlov became wholeheartedly committed to physiology. Pavlov then, as later, was rather oblivious to many of the cares of the everyday world. First his brother and then his wife had to perform such chores as buying Ivan Petrovich's clothes. His lack of concern for these matters was compensated for by his energetic devotion to his work. Pavlov's research progressed accordingly, and his success was such that he was awarded the Nobel Prize for his work on the digestive glands in 1904 (Gantt, 1928).

During the course of this work on the digestive system, Pavlov observed that glandular activity occurred before food was actually placed in the animal's mouth or passed along in the digestive system. The secretions were elicited by the sight or smell of food itself or by stimuli associated with the presentation of the food, such as the footfalls of the assistant who brought it to the animal. Pavlov became intrigued with these "psychical" secretions and, after some hesitation, began to focus on these phenomena in the salivary gland.

Pavlov was uneasy with mentalistic terminology and soon substituted a more objective language. He termed the reaction to food in the mouth an *unconditioned reflex*. The food was called an *unconditioned*

Figure 2.2

Ivan Petrovich Pavlov. From Pavlov, I. P., *Selected Works*, 1955. Reprinted by permission of Progress Publishers.

stimulus. When the salivary response came to be elicited by a previously inadequate stimulus, such as a footfall, a *conditioned reflex* was said to have developed. The new event that now elicited the salivation was termed a *conditioned stimulus.*[1] Pavlov and his colleagues quickly began describing important phenomena in conditioning (Pavlov, 1927). A few of the most basic are surveyed here.

Pavlov believed that any stimulus that acts on the sensory systems of an animal can become a conditioned stimulus. Furthermore, even the absence of a stimulus can serve as a conditioned stimulus. For example, if a usually beating metronome is turned off when food is to be presented, its silence can come to function as a conditioned stimulus. Another type of stimulus is time itself. In one experiment illustrating such *temporal conditioning,* food was presented at regular intervals. The dog came to salivate on the same schedule.

Secondary conditioned reflexes are possible if an inadequate or "neutral" stimulus is paired with a conditioned stimulus alone. If the neutral stimulus then also comes to elicit a conditioned response, it thus

---

[1] Pavlov's terms were *conditional* and *unconditional.* However, the conventional English translations are *conditioned* and *unconditioned.*

becomes a·secondary conditioned stimulus. For example, a black square was presented to a dog preceding the sound of the metronome, which was a conditioned stimulus for salivation. After ten trials, the black square itself elicited salivation. Conditioned reflexes of the third order were shown to be also possible, but they were limited to the defensive reactions, such as struggling in response to a shock to the skin.

If a conditioned stimulus is presented repeatedly without reinforcement—that is, without its associated unconditioned stimulus—it ceases to elicit the conditioned response. This weakening of the conditioned reflex is termed *experimental extinction.* If after some interval of time the conditioned stimulus is presented again, there is some degree of *spontaneous recovery* of the conditioned reflex.

Generalization occurs when stimuli that resemble the conditioned stimulus elicit the conditioned response to some extent. Such stimuli may elicit a degree of response even though they have never been paired with an unconditioned stimulus. For example, if tactile stimulation to a dog's foreleg were the conditioned stimulus, tactile stimuli to other skin areas could also elicit some response, even though these areas had never been stimulated during conditioning. There would be a *gradient of generalization* in that the conditioned response would be less the farther from the dog's foreleg the second tactile stimulus was applied. An animal can develop a *differentiation* between two similar stimuli if both stimuli are presented but only one is reinforced. However, if the discrimination required is very fine, the animal may fail to differentiate and may instead develop an *experimental neurosis.* For example, one dog squealed, wiggled, and attacked the apparatus when a circle/ellipse discrimination was made difficult.

As will become apparent later in this book, Pavlov's influence was widespread. Of particular interest here is Pavlov's effect on Russian behavioral science. Since Pavlov held most of psychology in low regard and, in its place, promoted the study of the physiology of higher nervous activity, his followers came to consider themselves not as psychologists but as students of higher nervous activity. To this day, there is a division in Russia between these scientists and psychologists, who represent a tradition concerned with problems in human behavior, such as psychopathology or developmental processes.

VLADIMIR MIKHAILOVICH BEKHTEREV

V. M. Bekhterev (Figure 2.3) received a medical degree from the Military Medical Academy in St. Petersburg two years before Pavlov (see Boring, 1950; Kimble, 1961; Yakovlev, 1959). He then studied under Flechsig, Wundt, Du Bois-Reymond, and Charcot. He was appointed to the Chair of Mental Diseases at the University of Kazan upon

Figure 2.3

Vladimir Mikhailovich Bekhterev. From Bekhterev, V. M. *General Principles of Human Reflexology,* International Publishers Co., Inc., 1928. Reprinted by permission.

his return from abroad. In 1893, he was given the Chair of Mental and Nervous Diseases at the Military Medical Academy in St. Petersburg. Bekhterev came to believe that psychology must be recreated. In 1904, he delivered a lecture entitled "Objective Psychology and Its Subject Matter." In 1906, he began experimental investigation of "association reflexes," studying shock-induced withdrawal and respiratory responses in dogs and humans. His text *Objective Psychology* was completed in 1912 and his *General Principles of Human Reflexology* was published in 1917. In these works, Bekhterev advocated the objective study of behavior and argued against the use of mentalistic terminology.

Bekhterev wanted to reform psychology rather than disregard it, as Pavlov would have done. Bekhterev was the first man to call himself an objective psychologist, and the translations of his *Objective Psychology* played an important role in the acceptance of similar views in America in the 1910s.

PSYCHOPHYSIOLOGY, PSYCHOLOGY, AND POLITICS

The later history of the study of behavior in Russia reflects the political events following the October revolution (Cole & Maltzman, 1969). The postrevolutionary fortunes of the two disciplines engaged the study of behavior have been quite different. The study of higher nervous activity, or psychophysiology as it has been called, found more favor with the materialistic Soviet government than it had with the czarist regime. Even during the years of hardship following the revolution, Pavlov was kept well supplied with equipment and laboratory food. Government support for psychophysiology continued through the bleak 1930s and the wartime 1940s. The year 1950 saw the celebration of the hundredth anniversary of Pavlov's birth and the canonization of Pavlov by the political leadership, apparently including Stalin himself. In a series of "scientific" meetings, the regime began to attack psychophysiologists who deviated from Pavlov's classical approach. Individual scientists were called upon to recant differing opinions. Stalin's death relieved some of this pressure, and Soviet psychophysiology has continued its growth.

The other discipline, psychology, fared worse under the Soviet government. After an initial period during which several schools of psychology flourished, the years of Stalin's power were marked by Party restrictions on what was permitted to stand as psychology. In 1950, along with the psychophysiologists, the psychologists were subjected to pressures to become more Pavlovian. Even after the end of this era, Soviet psychology remained strongly marked by its isolation and by the government's past efforts at "Pavlovianization."

Currently, Russian psychology and psychophysiology have been expanding and differentiating under fewer ideological restraints than in the past. But their history has had its effect. As Cole and Maltzman put it:

Coming upon Soviet psychology and psychological physiology for the first time is a little like Darwin first visiting the Galapagos. Different forms of species have evolved, as a result of isolation and interbreeding, which are adaptable to their environment. There are some exciting and stimulating surprises and some disappointments [1969, p. 37].

AMERICAN BEHAVIORISM

3

Entities should not be multiplied beyond necessity.   William of Occam

EARLY AMERICAN ANIMAL PSYCHOLOGY

Experimental psychology came from Germany to America in the 1880s. Its chief importers were the many young Americans who went to study at the new German psychology laboratories and then returned to introduce experimental psychology to their own universities. In Germany, experimental psychology had been founded by and was dominated by Wilhelm Wundt. In Wundt's view, experimental psychology was the science of mental content. Its proper method was *introspection* —examination of one's own mind and its contents—and the proper object of introspection was one's immediate experience. The problem of psychology was to identify the elements out of which immediate experience was formed and the ways in which those elements were joined to form experience. The manner in which the elements were assembled was held to be by *association, the principle by which ele*ments in spatial or temporal proximity would tend to join. Briefly, then, Wundt's psychology may be said to be characterized by mentalism, elementism, and associationism.

Wundt's experimental psychology did not find itself altogether at home in America. For, although some psychologists' thinking retained or assumed a Wundtian guise, some Americans had, or soon developed, differing outlooks. Gradually, a distinctive new school emerged, called *functionalism.* Functionalism was not so much a system of psychology as an approach to psychology. It meant that the interest of many American psychologists was not in the structure but in the *function* of the mind. Instead of searching for mental elements, the functionalists preferred to examine how the mind operated and how the mind helped man meet the demands of the world.

EDWARD L. THORNDIKE

Against the background of the new American functionalism and of the English mentalistic tradition of studying animal behavior, Edward L. Thorndike (Figure 3.1) helped to introduce animal experimentation into American psychology (Boring, 1950; Thorndike, 1936). As an undergraduate, Thorndike had become interested in psychology through his reading of William James' *Principles of Psychology.* In 1895, he

Figure 3.1

Edward L. Thorndike. From Murchison, C., *A History of Psychology in Autobiography,* Clark University Press, 1936. Reprinted by permission.

went to Harvard to study under James as a graduate student. Thorndike wanted to investigate animal intelligence, but neither his landlady nor the university was willing to provide him space to work with his laboratory chicks. Finally, James suggested that Thorndike use his cellar, and it was there, in large part, that experimental animal psychology began in America. However, Thorndike received no support from the university and had to maintain himself by serving as a tutor. When Columbia University came through with the offer of a fellowship, Thorndike accepted it and went to New York, carrying his two "most educated" chicks in a basket. At Columbia, Thorndike completed his doctoral thesis, one of the most influential dissertations ever written.

In his thesis, Thorndike (1898) set himself against the school of Romanes. He considered its anecdotal method to be inaccurate and prejudiced and its ascription of human characteristics to animals to be frequently unwarranted. Thorndike wrote that the followers of Romanes provided "a eulogy of animals" but never dealt with "animal stupidity."

To set matters right, Thorndike brought animals into the laboratory, where the unbiased and replicable experimental method could be used to elucidate the nature of animal intelligence. He employed two

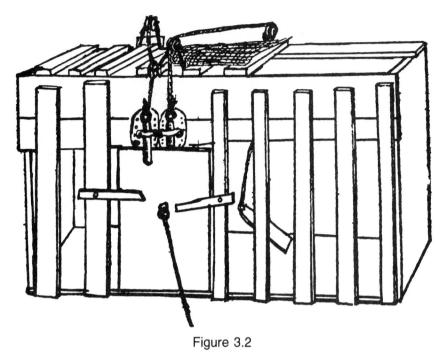

Figure 3.2

One of Thorndike's puzzle boxes. From Thorndike, 1898.

types of laboratory apparatus. The first was the puzzle box or escape box (Figure 3.2), a wooden cage with a door that could be opened from the inside by scratching a latch or pressing a lever or manipulating some other device. A hungry cat or dog would be introduced into the puzzle box and food placed outside the box. Thorndike observed the animal's behavior and recorded the *latency* of its response—that is, the time elapsing before a successful escape occurred. The second type of apparatus, which was used with chicks, consisted of various "pens" constructed out of books and other materials. The chicks were not food-deprived but were motivated to escape from the pens by their "dislike of loneliness."

The basic course of behavior in these two types of apparatus followed the same pattern. When initially introduced into the puzzle box, the cats and dogs would show a variety of responses, such as squirming, clawing, and biting. At some point, one of the captive animal's behaviors would succeed in operating the release mechanism, and the animal would escape and eat. Upon subsequent introductions, more and more of the animal's unsuccessful behaviors would drop out, and its successful movements would be perfected. The chicks learned to escape the pens in the same fashion: responses inappropriate for the situation, such as peeping and pecking, would drop out, and the successful response would come sooner. The results for the experiments with both the puzzle box and the pen were plotted on graphs like that shown in Figure 3.3.

Thorndike interpreted this learning process as follows: when an animal was first placed in a box or pen, various instincts were aroused through the discomfort produced by confinement or by food deprivation. By "instincts," Thorndike merely meant behaviors that an animal, without prior experience, emits in a situation. Thorndike suggested that, if the reader did not like his term, he could substitute "hocus-pocus" for "instinct" whenever he saw it. Along with the instincts, learned behaviors could be aroused if they were associated with anything resembling the situation. Both instinctive and learned activities were accompanied by *impulses.* According to Thorndike, an impulse

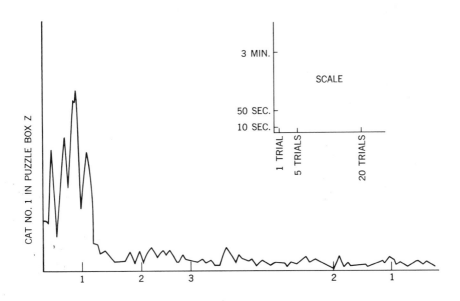

Figure 3.3.

Thorndike's "time-curve" for cat number 1 in puzzle box Z. As indicated on Thorndike's scale, the vertical axis shows the time it took the cat to escape and the horizontal axis represents the number of trials. The short vertical lines on the horizontal axis indicate that the cat was removed for a period of a day or longer; the number of days was noted if the period was longer than a day. After Thorndike, 1898.

is "the consciousness accompanying a muscular innervation apart from that feeling of the act which comes from seeing oneself move, from feeling one's body in a different position, etc. It is the direct feeling of doing" (1898, p. 15). The captive animal, then, typically had a "store of instinctive impulses," and when in the course of confinement it "hit" upon the successful response, the impulse for this response gradually became associated with the "sense impression of the interior of the box." The other instinctive impulses took a while to die out, but finally the association between sense impression and correct impulse was perfected. The unsuccessful impulses were said to be "stamped out," since they led nowhere, and the successful impulse was "stamped in" by the pleasure it produced.

After having produced this mentalistic account of what occurred in his laboratory, Thorndike brought up the principle of parsimony.

Presumably the reader has already seen budding out of this dogma a new possibility, a further simplification of these theories about animal consciousness. The possibility is that animals may have *no images or memories at all, no ideas to associate.* Perhaps the entire fact of association in animals is the presence of sense impressions with which are associated, by resultant pleasure, certain impulses, and that therefore, and therefore only, a certain situation brings forth a certain act [p. 73].

Actually, Thorndike stated that one did not have to go this far—one could maintain that ideas may be present in the animal mind—but Thorndike felt that they were neither necessary nor always present. Thorndike did not think that ideas were nonexistent in animals, even though he admitted that the theory of parsimony might lead one to that conclusion. It seemed too incredible that, when an animal's brain was excited by sense-impressions, it should not retain a consciousness of them in imagination and in memory.

To summarize, Thorndike represents an advance in the development of the study of animal behavior that stems from Darwin and progresses through Romanes and Morgan. Thorndike's contributions lie in his helping introduce laboratory experimentation in America, seeing that much animal intelligence was the result of trial-and-error learning, and emphasizing the importance of reward in learning.

In the years immediately following the publication of Thorndike's thesis, interest in animal psychology quickened. The period from 1899 to 1903 saw the establishment of laboratories of comparative psychology at Clark, Harvard, and Chicago. By 1910, ten universities possessed laboratories, and almost 20 offered courses in comparative psychology (Boring, 1950).

JOHN B. WATSON

At this time, John B. Watson (Figure 3.4) made his appearance in psychology. Watson took his Ph.D. at Chicago, the center of functionalism, in 1903. Watson was an enthusiastic animal worker from the beginning of his career.

With animals I was at home. I felt that in studying them, I was keeping close to biology with my feet on the ground. More and more the thought presented itself: Can't I find by watching their behavior everything that the other students are finding out by using [introspective observers]? . . . I broached this to my colleagues as early as 1904, but received little encouragement [Watson, 1936, p. 276].

Watson also became annoyed with those who considered psychology to be primarily the study of mental experience.

It is [their assumption] that introspection is the method *par excellence* by means of which mental states can be manipulated for purposes of psychology. On this assumption, behavior data (including under this term everything which goes under the name of comparative psychology) have

Figure 3.4

John B. Watson. From Murchison, C., *A History of Psychology in Autobiography,* Clark University Press, 1936. Reprinted by permission.

no value *per se.* They possess significance only in so far as they may throw light upon conscious states [1913, pp. 158–159].

Especially irritating to Watson was the argument that, in order to make data from animal behavior relevant for psychology, one had to translate these data into human mentalistic terminology. This translation was made on the basis of the analogy of human experience—that is, what one might suppose a human would feel if he had only the discriminative and motor capacities of a fly, for example.

Watson rejected not only this approach to animal psychology but even the sacrosanct tenet that introspection was the key method for human psychology.

Psychology as the behaviorist views it is a purely objective experimental branch of natural science. Its theoretical goal is the prediction and control of behavior. Introspection forms no essential part of its methods, nor is the scientific value of its data dependent upon the readiness with which they lend themselves to interpretation in terms of consciousness. The behaviorist, in his efforts to get a unitary scheme of animal response, recognizes no dividing line between man and brute. The behavior of man, with all its refinement and complexity, forms only a part of the behaviorist's total scheme of investigation [p. 158].

With these words from Watson's manifesto of 1913, a clamorous battle was joined among the schools of experimental psychology.

Watson relied on the concepts of instinct and learning to account for much of behavior. In 1914, Watson's behavioristic definition of instinct was "a combination of congenital responses unfolding serially under appropriate stimulation" (p. 106). Instincts were developed during the evolution of a species. Habit differed from instinct in "the origin of the *pattern* (number and localizations of simple reflex arcs involved) and the *order* (temporal relations) of the unfolding of the elements composing that pattern" (p. 184). In habit, the pattern and order of reflexes were acquired during the lifetime of the individual; once perfected, they functioned in "all particulars" in the same way as instincts.

The acquisition of habits could be understood in terms of three principles. According to the principle of *frequency,* the most successful movement tends to be acquired because it is engaged in relatively more frequently than if it were not effective. In the case of the puzzle box, for example, the sequence of acts is always stopped by the successful movement. Since it is invariably given, the successful movement is more probable than it would be otherwise. According to the principle of *recency,* the animal tends to learn the successful movement because it is the last response in the situation. In other words, when the animal is reintroduced to the problem, it would tend to reproduce the escape response because escape was the most recent response it had given in that context. The principle of *substitution* works on a different basis:

if one stimulus is presented with a second stimulus that elicits some response, the first will also come to elicit the response, thus substituting for the second. This principle was, of course, Pavlov's.

A few years later, Watson (1919) began to criticize instinct as a sufficient explanatory notion for much of human behavior. Instead, Watson emphasized learning as an explanatory principle. Watson's theory was paralleled by his research. He began to study the conditioning of fear responses in human infants.

Watson's career in psychology was disrupted when he was forced to resign from Johns Hopkins in the aftermath of sensational publicity surrounding his divorce. Watson went to New York, "stranded economically and to some extent emotionally," an academic who "knew nothing of life outside the walls of a university" (Watson, 1936, p. 279). Finally, through the offices of a friend, Watson obtained employment in the advertising business with J. Walter Thompson. Ever the psychologist, Watson spent a summer as a clerk in Macy's department store to study consumer behavior. Within four years, Watson was promoted to vice president at the Thompson agency, and he remained in the advertising field until he retired. Although Watson's scholarly output was reduced after his entry into the commercial world, he continued to write occasional articles and even managed to produce three more books.

Even though Watson was forced out of the academic life, behaviorism became the dominant force in American academic psychology. It should be noted that this trend was not entirely due to Watson's influence; the *Zeitgeist*, the spirit of the times, was moving in favor of behaviorism. Not only did America become behavioristic; it also preserved a Watsonian emphasis on animal experimentation. It can be truly said that much of American experimental psychology became experimental animal psychology. Experimental animal psychology itself was transformed. The white rat grew in popularity until it displaced most other experimental species. Indeed, from the 1930s to the 1950s, experimental psychology became in large part the study of the white rat, the psychologists' "fuzzy white test tube."

A further important change occurred. Although by the 1920s Watson had largely discounted human instincts, he still accepted the concept of instincts in animals. However, even the notion of instinct in general began to come into question around the time of Watson's departure from Johns Hopkins University. A radical behavioristic position developed that argued that the concept of instinct ought to be dropped altogether. Zing-Yang Kuo (1922) exemplified the radical position at this time. For Kuo, the only behaviors that possibly were unlearned were the reaction units, or muscular movements, present around the time of birth. Through learning, these reaction units became integrated temporally and sequentially into complex behaviors, some of which were erroneously termed instincts.

Thus, in America in the 1910s and 1920s, there arose a hard-headed animal psychology. It rejected slippery, impalpable mentalistic concepts and discarded the facile, simplistic explanatory device of instinct. The laboratory was its home, and the white rat became its experimental subject. As time passed, it focused more and more on the process of learning.

LATER AMERICAN ANIMAL PSYCHOLOGY

The 1930s saw the emergence of the general theories of learning and motivation that came to dominate much of experimental psychology until the 1950s. Innumerable experiments with rats were generated by these theories and the points of contrast between them. Perhaps the most prominent theorists of these decades were Tolman, Hull, Guthrie, and Skinner. In this text, limitations of space compel me to treat only one theorist, Skinner. It should be remembered that there were rather wide differences between the theorists of the time, and therefore one theorist cannot be considered truly representative of the others. It should also be stressed that there were other important animal psychologists of the time who were not identified with these mainstream viewpoints.

B. F. SKINNER

B. F. Skinner has tread on many psychologists' toes in his long career. In contrast with some prominent neobehaviorists, Skinner came to believe that elaborate theories of learning and motivation were often unnecessary and misleading (Skinner, 1950). Instead, Skinner believed that psychologists should manipulate variables in order to study their effect on behavior. Furthermore, Skinner thought that the complex statistics and research methods used by many of his colleagues were poor tools for the study of behavior. All of this was anathema to the psychologist who was testing hypotheses derived from some theoretical system using elegant experimental designs. In addition, Skinner was not satisfied to remain in the laboratory: he plunged into the real world with experimentation and behavioral engineering. He told protesting teachers and psychiatrists how to run their affairs.

Although Skinner disavowed elaborate theorization, he himself has made many assumptions about behavior. These assumptions determine in large degree the way in which Skinnerians approach behavior. For example, Skinner (1938, 1953, 1957) has always distinguished two types of conditioning. The first type is the classical conditioning of Pavlov and

Bekhterev. Initially, this type was called *Type S conditioning*, and later it was termed *respondent conditioning*. The traditional language is used here to describe this class of learning. A *neutral stimulus* is presented, along with an *unconditioned stimulus* that elicits an *unconditioned response*. After several trials, the neutral stimulus becomes a *conditioned stimulus* as it starts to elicit a *conditioned response*. Responses involved in this type of conditioning are called *respondents*. Such reflexive responses are seen as chiefly involved with internal processes or equilibrium and are not viewed as playing a determining role in most of the organism's interactions with the world. For this reason, Skinner has tended to de-emphasize respondent behavior.

Skinner (1938) stresses the second type of conditioning: *Type R* or *operant conditioning*. This type of conditioning is exemplified by the behavior of the rat in the Skinner box (Figure 3.5). When we place a hungry rat in the Skinner box, it will emit many responses. It will rear, walk, sniff, groom, and so forth. Occasionally it will touch the bar on one of the walls of the Skinner box, and, somewhat less frequently, it will push the bar down. If the rat is left undisturbed in the box, it will

Figure 3.5

Discrimination in a Skinner box. The rat is learning to press the bar whenever one of the two lights is on. Photograph by Ronald Hoffman.

perform these barpresses at some given rate. If the food magazine is then activated so that a barpress will cause a bit of food to be dispensed, there will be a change in the rat's behavior. The rate of barpressing will increase until the rat is responding at a steady higher rate. If the rat is removed and returned the next day, it will shortly begin to respond at the same steady relatively high rate of the previous day.

In Skinnerian language, this process may be described as follows. After being introduced to the experimental chamber, the rat *emits* many responses. Some of these responses depress the bar: pressing downward with the body, pushing with two paws, or even falling backward in the proper orientation. Any response that depresses the bar, no matter what its form, belongs to the class of *operant* responses called barpresses. Each of these barpresses, or *operants,* is equivalent, since it operates on the environment in the same fashion. Before the food magazine is activated, the rate at which the barpresses occur is called an *operant level. Operant conditioning* is the procedure through which we increase the rate at which the operant is emitted. The procedure in this case consists of making a food pellet *contingent* on the operant response. Presentation of a reward such as a pellet is termed *reinforcement.*

The rate and pattern of the rat's responses can be changed through the use of schedules of *intermittent reinforcement.* For example, if, instead of reinforcing the rat every time, we now reinforce it every third time it presses the bar, its rate of response will increase. In this case, we have switched from continuous reinforcement to a *fixed-ratio reinforcement schedule.* The highest rates of response are possible on a *variable-ratio schedule,* when the number of responses required for a reinforcement varies but averages to some chosen value. In a *fixed-interval schedule,* we allow the rat to be reinforced only at set intervals; for example, we might reinforce the first barpress that occurs at the end of each minute. Under such a schedule, a rat will come to respond more rapidly as the time for reinforcement nears but then will shift to a lower rate of responding after its first successful response.

If we get tired of watching the rat respond, we can stop him by ceasing to give reinforcement. This procedure is called *extinction.* After a while, the rat's response rate will return to near its operant level. The rat's *resistance to extinction*—that is, its persistence in responding when it is not reinforced—will be greater if the animal has been on an intermittent rather than a continuous reinforcement schedule.

We can also teach the rat to respond only when we want him to do so. If we turn a small light on above the food cup and reinforce the rat only for responses given when the light is on, the rat will come to emit nearly all of his responses when this stimulus is present. The rat has thus learned a *discrimination,* and his response is controlled by the appearance of a *discriminative stimulus,* which has in the past been the occasion when response yielded reward.

A discriminative stimulus becomes a reinforcer, and it may function like the pellet in changing behavior. The discriminative stimulus is termed a *conditioned* or *secondary* reinforcer, since it becomes a reinforcer only through its association with some other reinforcer. This other reinforcer may be another conditioned reinforcer, or it may be an *unconditioned* or *primary reinforcer* like food. Conditioned reinforcers are important because they can be presented to an organism immediately after a behavior that we want to make more frequent. Any *delay of reinforcement* makes operant conditioning difficult or impossible.

Using secondary reinforcers, we can *shape* elaborate *chains* of behavior. Suppose that a rat has learned to press a bar on a fixed-ratio schedule of three whenever the small light is on. We want to train the rat to touch his nose to one of the rear corners of the Skinner box and chain this behavior to the *discriminated operant* the rat has already acquired. That is, we want to form the chain of nose contact, light on, three barpresses, and eating. It is quite easy to shape the nose contact: first we make our secondary reinforcer, light onset, contingent on the rat's movements away from the bar; then, once the frequency of moving away increases, we reinforce only movements that take the rat to the corner we have selected; then we reinforce upward movement when the rat arrives in the corner; finally, we reinforce only actual nose contact in the corner. Thus by a series of *successive approximations* we can readily shape a new behavior and chain it to an older one.

The behavior of a well-trained rat on such a chain is striking. It appears to be "deliberate" and "purposeful" as well as "clever." The rat touches the corner "to turn on the light," goes to the bar, which it depresses with three "efficient" strokes of the paw, quickly eats its pellet, and then starts through the same cycle. But, as the rat's trainers, we know that this performance is merely the result of a sequence of reinforcement contingencies.

Quite lengthy chains are possible, even with a rat. Barnabus, a rat who studied at a college in the eastern United States, is described in the following account.

When a light flashes at the lower left-hand side of the cage, Barnabus scampers to a rising circular mesh pathway and runs up to a first landing, where he crosses a moat to the bottom of a 16-step "ladder." He climbs the ladder to the second platform. There with his teeth and paws he hauls a chain that is attached to a small red car. Having brought the car to him, Barnabus climbs in and pedals away. When the car reaches the bottom of a stairway, he gets out, runs upstairs to reach a third platform, and squeezes through a glass tube 17 inches long. Barnabus then enters an elevator, and as it descends, he yanks with his front paws and teeth a chain that raises the flag of his university. (The students at this point often stand at attention, some with moist eyes.) When he reaches the bottom of the cage, Barnabus presses a bar. A buzzer sounds and he is free to eat all the food he can during a one-minute period. Hail the powers of reinforcement [Kendler, 1968, pp. 295–297; references to figures deleted]!*

RECENT TRENDS IN AMERICAN ANIMAL PSYCHOLOGY

Contemporary animal psychologists are becoming more and more difficult to characterize. There are still Skinnerians and Hullians of different types, as well as followers of more recent theorists. But since the early 1950s there has been a dramatic growth in the number of other kinds of animal psychologists. One is the student of animal behavior who compares the performances of many species in standard experimental situations. Another is the physiological psychologist. This psychologist typically studies the relationship of the nervous system to behaviors exhibited by animals in the laboratory. A third type may perhaps be described as problem-oriented. For example, a great number of workers have been studying pain and schedule-induced aggression. Other animal psychologists have even begun to leave the laboratory and study their subjects under natural conditions. This chapter will conclude with a discussion of the comparative psychology of learning. Several of the other contributions made by contemporary students of animal psychology will be considered in subsequent chapters.

COMPARATIVE STUDIES OF LEARNING

Experimental psychologists who compare the behavior of different species have tended, as might be expected, to investigate learning in these animals. Thorndike was the first experimentalist to make this kind of comparison. In addition to his doctoral studies with chicks, cats, and dogs, discussed earlier, Thorndike worked with fish (1899), monkeys (1901), and children (1904). From this research, Thorndike (1911) concluded that there were two laws of learning. The *law of effect* states that a response will become more firmly connected with a situation if it is followed by a satisfier, but that this connection will be weakened if it is followed by discomfort. The *law of exercise* states that a response will become more firmly connected with a situation in proportion to the frequency, vigor, and duration of the response produced in that situation. Thorndike wrote that, although the behavior of animals varies

---

*From H. H. Kendler, *Basic Psychology, Second Edition,* copyright © 1968, by W. A. Benjamin, Inc., Menlo Park, California. Reprinted by permission.

because of sensory, motor, and motivational differences, the two principles of learning apply across species.

If my analysis is true the evolution of behavior is a rather simple matter.
Formally the crab, fish, turtle, cat, monkey, and baby have very similar
intellects and characters. All are systems subject to change by the law of
exercise and effect [1911, p. 280].

It was the explicit or implicit acceptance of the view that learning
was essentially similar across species that allowed psychologists to concentrate their research on the white rat. Skinner (1956), for example,
showed that a complex schedule of reinforcement would generate the
same patterns of responses in the pigeon, the rat, and the monkey, and
commented "Which is which? It doesn't matter."

Recently, however, Bitterman and his colleagues have re-exam-
ined the assumption that learning is essentially similar in different
vertebrate taxa.[1] Comparing the performance of classes of animals on
complex tasks, Bitterman (1960, 1965a, 1965b, 1968) suggested that
qualitative differences in learning can be distinguished. One of these
differences is revealed in the *serial reversal* task. In this type of task,
animals are first trained to select one of two stimuli. For example, an
African mouthbrooder, a cichlid fish, may be rewarded for pressing one
of a pair of illuminated discs lowered into its aquarium. One can train
the fish to press either the right or the left disc; this is called a spatial
or position discrimination. Alternatively, one can train the animal to
select targets varying in their appearance; this is called a visual discrimination. The animal is trained in either the spatial or the visual problem
until it reaches some preset *criterion;* for example, the fish might be
required to make five correct responses in a row. After that point, the
experimenter introduces a reversal: the positive or rewarded alternative in the task becomes negative and the negative alternative becomes
positive. This cycle repeats itself: the animal is repeatedly trained to
criterion and then reversed. According to Bitterman, a fish trained in
either the spatial or the visual problem shows no improvement over
reversals; that is, the fish does not show any progressive decrease in the
number of trials it requires to learn each new reversal. When a rat is
tested in an analogous apparatus, there is a striking difference: the rat
shows substantial improvement with successive reversals. It takes
progressively less time for the rat to achieve criterion on each new
reversal.

[1]A *taxon* (plural: *taxa*) refers to any group of animals in the zoological system of classification. A taxon can be a subspecies, a species, a genus, a family, and so forth. The related
term *taxonomy* means either a particular system of classification or the study of classification.

A second way in which fish and rat differ is in terms of *probability matching.* Suppose that, instead of rewarding the positive disc on 100% of the trials, one rewards one disc on 70% of the trials and the other on 30% of the trials. Provided that the distribution of rewards is exact, fish tend to match probabilities; that is, they choose the 70% alternative on 70% of the trials and the 30% alternative on 30% of the trials. The fish do not adopt the strategy that maximizes reward, because maximum reward would be obtained by responding to the 70% alternative on 100% of the trials. The fish's strategy is nonoptimal because, even in the relatively short run, an animal will get the most rewards by always responding to the alternative where 70% of its responses will be rewarded and by never responding to an alternative where only 30% of its responses will be rewarded. Rats do approximate the strategy that maximizes reward: they tend to respond at 90% or better to the more frequently rewarded alternative (see Figure 3.6).

Research on other species trained in analogous tasks indicated that some behave like rats and others like fish. Bitterman summarized his

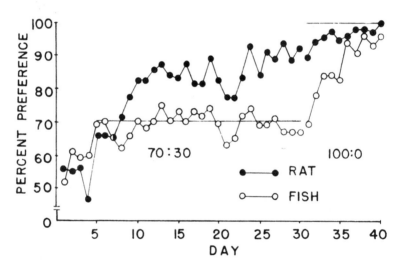

Figure 3.6

Preference for the more rewarded alternative in the fish and the rat, with reinforcement distributed 70:30 or 100:0. The preference of the trained fish matches the probability of reinforcement, whereas the preference of the rat is usually for the more rewarded alternative. See text for further explanation. From Bitterman, M. E., Wodinsky, J., & Candland, D. K. Some comparative psychology. *American Journal of Psychology*, 1958, *71*, 94–110. Reprinted by permission.

Table 3.1

Summary of learning performances in the monkey, rat, pigeon, turtle, and fish. F indicates performance at the level of a fish, and R indicates performance at the level of a rat. Adapted from Bitterman, M. E. Phyletic differences in learning. *American Psychologist,* 1965, *20,* 396–410. Copyright 1965 by the American Psychological Association. Reprinted by permission.

ANIMAL	SPATIAL PROBLEMS		VISUAL PROBLEMS	
	REVERSAL	PROBABILITY	REVERSAL	PROBABILITY
Monkey	R	R	R	R
Rat	R	R	R	R
Pigeon	R	R	R	F
Turtle	R	R	F	F
Fish	F	F	F	F

work in a table that showed whether the performances of monkey, pigeon, or turtle resembled that of rat or that of fish (see Table 3.1). Bitterman recognized that this table was provisional; not enough species had been studied, and the classification of performances as ratlike or fishlike was not sufficiently refined.

The latest research has suggested that some modifications ought to be made in Bitterman's table of differences (see review by Mackintosh, 1969). Reversal learning may be considered first. In the case of fish, typically no improvement is seen in the reversal task when Bitterman's basic apparatus is used. However, if this apparatus is modified so that food is presented at a discrete place and not merely dropped into the aquarium, a slight improvement in habit reversal can be demonstrated (Mackintosh & Cauty, 1971). (See Figure 3.7.)

A single study (Squier, 1969) performed using two oscars (a cichlid fish) suggests that even greater reversal improvement may be possible in the higher bony fishes. Overall, however, the evidence is that fishes show either no improvement or only slight improvement in serial reversal. Birds, on the other hand, nearly always show serial reversal improvement, with mynahs, magpies, and parrots performing better than pigeons, domestic chicks, and quail.

In probability learning, fish do tend to match probabilities. However, Bitterman's contention that pigeons perform like fish in visual-probability problems and like rats in spatial-probability problems does not rest on firm ground. Rather, the evidence is now clear that pigeons respond in both visual- and spacial-probability tasks by exceeding a matching level of performance but not by maximizing: that is, these birds typically select the more rewarded alternative more frequently than they would if they were probability matching but less frequently

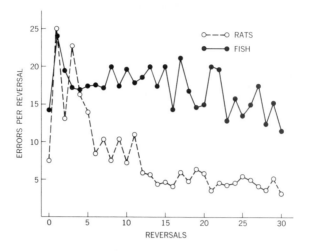

Figure 3.7

Improvement over reversals in rats and fish. From
Mackintosh, N. J., & Cauty, A. Spatial reversal learn-
ing in rats, pigeons, and goldfish. *Psychonomic
Science,* 1971, *22,* 282. Reprinted by permission.

than would rats (Mackintosh, 1969; Mackintosh, Lord, & Little, 1971).
The performance of pigeons is not representative of all birds; it has
been shown that day-old domestic chicks, for example, can rapidly
develop ratlike maximizing on visual discriminations.

In summary, this research on the classic question of the evolution
of animal intelligence indicates that there are contrasts between the
performance of rats and that of certain species of birds and bony fishes
in at least two complex tasks. However, until enough species are tested
with a sufficient variety of apparatus, any generalizations about the
abilities of different classes of animals must be limited. The evidence at
hand does suggest that the performances of various species form a
continuum without discontinuities, and this observation makes it difficult to argue that different classes of animals possess qualitatively different learning mechanisms. Indeed, the most impressive finding from the
comparative study of learning is not the essentially quantitative differences in performance that exist but, on the contrary, the great similarity
in the behavior of different animal groups in many learning situations.
This similarity can extend even to the details of their performance. For
example, creatures as diverse as the blue jay and the rhesus monkey
show remarkable parallels in repeated object discriminations (Kamil,
Lougee, & Shulman, 1973).

CLASSICAL ETHOLOGY 4

HISTORICAL DEVELOPMENT

Around the turn of the twentieth century, the zoologist C. O. Whitman (Figure 4.1) was studying doves and pigeons at the University of Chicago. Whitman recognized behavior patterns characteristic of each species (see Carr, 1919; Whitman, 1899). For example, in the now extinct passenger pigeon, the male was observed to display to females by calling loudly as it drew back its head and "flirted" its wings by moving them upward and forward. (A *display* is a behavior that serves as a social signal.) In the white-winged pigeon, territorial display by both male and female was seen to take the form of jerking the tail, bristling the feathers, and calling with the beak open. Comparisons of similarities and differences in such "instincts" proved useful to Whitman in working out the zoological classification of these birds. Whitman

Figure 4.1

Charles Otis Whitman, 1882. From Lapham's History of Woodstock, Maine.

suggested that instincts should be studied from the standpoint of evolution, just as were bodily structures.

Whitman's student Wallace Craig (Figure 4.2) also observed "instinctive" behavior on the basis of these observations. For Craig, "each instinct involves an element of appetite, or aversion, or both" (1918, p. 91). An appetite was defined as

a state of agitation which continues so long as a certain stimulus, which may be called the appeted stimulus, is absent. When the appeted stimulus is at length received, it stimulates a consummatory reaction, after which the appetitive behaviour ceases and is succeeded by a state of relative rest [p. 91].

An example of an appetite was seen in the young male dove's behavior when he first locates a nesting site.

The first thing the observer sees is that the dove, while standing on his perch, spontaneously assumes the nest-calling attitude, his body tilted forward, head down, as if his neck and breast were already touching the hollow of a nest (incipient consummatory action), and in this attitude he sounds the nest-call. But he shows dissatisfaction, as if the bare perch were not a comfortable situation for this nest-dedicating attitude. He shifts

Figure 4.2

Wallace Craig. Photograph courtesy of Raymond H. Folger Library, University of Maine, Orono.

about until he finds a corner which more or less fits his body while in the tilted posture; he is seldom satisfied with his first corner, but tries another and another. If now an appropriate nest-box or a ready-made nest is put into his cage, this inexperienced dove does not recognize it as a nest, but sooner or later he tries it, as he has tried all other places for nest-calling, and in such trial the nest evidently gives him a strong and satisfying stimulation (the appeted stimulus) which no other situation has given him [see Figure 4.3]. In the nest his attitude becomes extreme; he abandons himself to an orgy of nest-calling (complete consummatory action), turning now this way and now that in the hollow, palpating the straws with his feet, wings, breast, neck, and beak, and rioting in the wealth of new, luxurious stimuli. He no longer wanders restlessly in search of new nesting situations, but remains satisfied with his present highly stimulating nest [Craig, 1918, p. 98].

Craig defined an aversion as

a state of agitation which continues as long as a certain stimulus, referred to as the disturbing stimulus, is present; but which ceases, being replaced by a state of relative rest, when that stimulus has ceased to act on the sense-organs [p. 91].

An example of an aversion is observed in the "so-called jealousy" of the male dove before his mate lays her eggs. The male will aggressively drive an intruder away from his mate or will more gently drive his mate away from the intruder.

Appetites are accompanied by certain tendencies to act in some ways but not in others. Sometimes an appetite will cause a series of

Figure 4.3

Crouching male ring dove nest-calling before his mate. Original photograph from Craig (1909).

reflexes to occur, but, typically, the early and middle segments of behavior sequences that appear to be reflexive are in fact learned. However, all such sequential patterns end with a "consummatory action" that is innate.

When a motivated animal has no innate chain of reflexes available and has not yet acquired a learned sequence of behavior, it will engage in appetitive trial-and-error behavior such as that described in the nest-seeking dove. This behavior is often accompanied by "incipient consummatory actions," even though the "appeted stimulus" is not yet present. Once the appeted stimulus is obtained, the complete consummatory action occurs.

Like appetites, aversions are sometimes accompanied by some "innately determined reaction" adapted to eliminating the disturbing stimulus. However, with some aversions, learning like that seen in appetites occurs: the birds emit "trials" until one trial succeeds in getting rid of the disturbing stimulus or obtaining the appeted stimulus. When reintroduced to the same situation, the animal will tend to repeat the successful trial.

Appetites show other interesting characteristics. They are largely dependent on physiological factors, although an environmental stimulus can be their "immediate excitant." If an appetite cannot be satisfied because there is no appeted stimulus present, consummatory action will sometimes occur in response to "an abnormal or inadequate stimulus." Even in this case, "the tension of the appetite is relieved, its energy discharged, and the organism shows satisfaction" (p. 102).

Unfortunately, for a long time after Craig did this work, there was little further concern with behavior at this level in American zoology; only quite recently has there been renewed interest in the theory of animal behavior.

In European zoology, however, a similar development began that had more lasting consequences (see Hess, 1962). In 1910, Oskar Heinroth independently came to some of the same conclusions that Whitman had come to earlier. Heinroth described various movement patterns in ducks and noted similarities between taxa. He demonstrated that behaviors in different groups could be *homologous*—that is, that they evolved from a common ancestral pattern. This demonstration revealed that behavioral characteristics were of value in understanding taxonomy (Hess, 1962).

In the 1930s, Konrad Lorenz, a student of Heinroth, began to build his own theory, drawing on the behavioral data that were accumulating and on some of the ideas of Craig, Heinroth, and others (see Lorenz, 1970). Other European zoologists became interested in animal behavior, and the pace of research started to quicken. The years after World War II saw the coming of age of the classical school of ethology. Lorenz's paper "The Comparative Method of Studying Innate Behavior Patterns" (1950) and Tinbergen's *The Study of Instinct* (1951) represent the views of this new school. Since these years, a split has emerged in the school. The views of some ethologists, including Lorenz, have changed little, whereas the views of others, including Tinbergen, have been substantially modified. Because the contemporary proponents of classical ethology are still vigorously defending and promoting their positions, and because the outlooks of "revisionist" ethologists have evolved from classical ethology, we will examine the original school of the 1950s. Then we will turn to two modifications in its concepts that have been suggested by the "revisionists."

THE SCHOOL OF CLASSICAL ETHOLOGY

CLASSICAL ETHOLOGY'S DESCRIPTIVE LANGUAGE

Classical ethology is based largely on observations and experimentation under field or seminatural conditions. Ideally, the first goal of the researcher is to form a catalog of the behaviors of his subject species under such conditions. This catalog is called an *ethogram*.

According to the classical ethologists, many of the behaviors in such catalogs take the form of *fixed-action patterns*. These patterns are equivalent to the consummatory behavior patterns described by Craig and are likewise considered to be innate. Moreover, the sequence of behaviors in a fixed-action pattern does not vary, and sensory feedback from the constituent movements of the pattern does not influence its performance. More variable *appetitive* behavior may precede the expression of a fixed-action pattern. Consider the example of the peregrine falcon (Tinbergen, 1951).

The hunting of a peregrine falcon usually begins with relatively random roaming around its hunting territory, visiting and exploring many different places miles apart. This first phase of appetitive behaviour may lead to different ways of catching prey, each dependent on special stimulation by a potential prey. It is continued until such a special stimulus situation is found: a flock of teal executing flight manoeuvres, a sick gull swimming apart from the flock, or even a running mouse. Each of these situations may cause the falcon to abandon its "random" searching. But what follows then is not yet a consummatory action, but appetitive behaviour of a new, more specialized and more restricted kind. The flock of teal releases a series of sham attacks serving to isolate one or a few individuals from the main body of the flock. Only after this is achieved is the final swoop released, followed by capturing, killing, plucking and eating, which is a relatively simple and stereotyped chain of consummatory acts. The sick gull may provoke the release of sham attacks, tending to force it to fly up; if this fails the falcon may deftly pick it up from the water surface. A small mammal may release simple straightforward approach and subsequent capturing, etc. Thus we see that the generalized appetitive behaviour was continued until a special stimulus situation interrupted the random searching and released one of the several possible and more specific types of appetitive behaviour. This in its turn was continued until the changing stimulus situation released the swoop, a still more specific type of appetitive behaviour, and this finally led to the chain of consummatory acts [pp. 106-107].*

Taxes are either oriented movements or static orientations toward some source of stimulation. For example, the greylag goose retrieves an egg that has rolled out of its nest by reaching out and pulling the egg back under its head. The goose makes small lateral motions that keep the egg from rolling away. These small movements are considered taxes because their orientation depends on sensory feedback from the egg. In contrast, the drawing back of the head is regarded as a fixed-action pattern. This movement is so classified because it can be demonstrated that the response, once released, is independent of sensory feedback: the goose continues a simple backward motion even if the egg is removed from under its bill.

Classical ethologists have restricted their study of stimulus factors largely to *key,* or *sign, stimuli.* Key stimuli are those that release a fixed-action pattern or other instinctive behavior. An example of the functioning of a key stimulus can be seen in the toad *Bufo bufo* (Eibl-Eibesfeldt, 1970). Small moving stimuli release visual fixation and snapping in the toad. The release of these behaviors by such stimuli can be demonstrated experimentally: the newly metamorphosed toad will fixate on and snap at any number of small moving objects, including stones and bits of paper manipulated by the ethologist; however, when the movement of any of these stimuli is stopped, the toad usually fixates for a period and then ceases to be controlled by the stimulus.

Confusingly, *releasers* are often distinguished as a subclass of key stimuli. Releasers are commonly defined as those behaviors, behavior consequences, or aspects of the body that have evolved to function in communication. For example, consider the conspicuous releaser that elicits aggression in defense of territory in the European robin (*Erithacus rubecula*). Lack (1943) has shown that this aggression is released by an intruder's red breast feathers: a stuffed young male robin with these feathers removed is a generally ineffective stimulus, but a tuft of red breast feathers alone will release attack behavior.

Note that, in both examples, the animals do not react to all the aspects of the stimulus that they are capable of discriminating. Inexperienced toads strike at any moving object; however, they can learn to avoid striking at noxious-tasting insects or inedible stimuli waved about

*From Tinbergen, N., *The Study of Instinct,* 1951. Reprinted by permission of The Clarendon Press, Oxford.

by the ethologist. Robins use all kinds of visual information in their other behaviors, yet they attack a bodiless tuft of feathers. These facts indicate that key stimuli may comprise only a few characteristics of the real stimulus object. By presenting animals with a series of stimuli, the ethologist can discover what these critical characteristics are. The ethologist can even create stimuli that are more effective than the natural ones in releasing various behaviors. A classic example of the effect of such *supernormal* or *superoptimal* stimuli can be seen in the oystercatcher *Haemotopus ostralegus*. If the oystercatcher is presented with an artificial egg that is twice the length of its own, it will prefer the ethologist's creation to an egg of natural size (Tinbergen, 1951). Its attempts to sit on such an egg appear quite awkward.

Many of the behaviors that provide key stimuli in animal communication appear to have evolved from basically noncommunicative behaviors by the process called *ritualization*. The original behavior sequence is altered: certain elements may be exaggerated, repeated, and stereotyped, whereas other elements may be omitted. The new sequence may appear in different stimulus situations and under different motivational conditions. For example, many threat behaviors appear to have evolved from actual attack: according to Eibl-Eibesfeldt (1970), the human act of stamping the feet in anger is probably a ritualized attack behavior. *Displacement* activity—apparently out-of-context behavior that occurs in conflict situations—is another source of communicative behavior. Preening or grooming that occurs when the animal is subject to conflicting motivations, for instance, often evolves into displays.

Key stimuli and fixed-action patterns can alternate to produce a *reaction chain*. For example, the male three-spined stickleback reacts to a gravid female by swimming toward her in a series of zigzags (see Figure 4.4). If this action releases a "curious head-up posture" in the female, the male responds by swimming directly toward the nest. The female follows him to the nest, where he begins to thrust rapidly with his snout into the entrance. During these thrusts, he turns on his side and elevates his dorsal spines. The female reacts by swimming into the nest. The male then repeatedly prods the female, and this action leads to her laying her eggs. The female leaves the nest, and the male proceeds to fertilize the eggs. This entire chain takes about a minute. As is apparent, each response in the chain produces a new stimulus that releases the partner's behavior. The partner's behavior, in turn, constitutes a new stimulus situation, and so forth (Tinbergen, 1952).

THEORETICAL NOTIONS

The classical ethologists have introduced several theoretical concepts. The *innate releasing mechanism* (IRM) is postulated to be the special neurosensory mechanism that releases a reaction whenever the

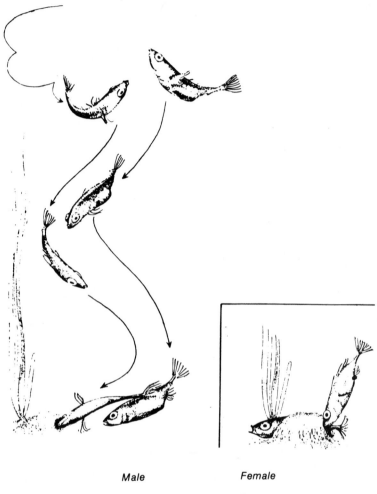

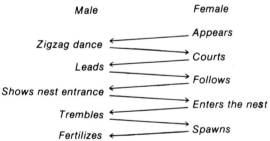

Figure 4.4

Chain of mating responses in the three-spined stickleback. From Tinbergen, N., *The Study of Instinct*, 1951. Reprinted by permission of The Clarendon Press, Oxford.

appropriate key stimuli are present. *Action-specific energy* (or some similar force) is presumed to control the IRM. Action-specific energy accumulates whenever a fixed-action pattern does not occur. When the action-specific energy reaches a certain level, it activates the IRM so that, if the proper key stimuli appear, the fixed-action pattern will be released and the energy will be discharged. Should the key stimuli not appear, the buildup of action-specific energy will further sensitize the IRM so that less than optimal key stimuli will release the reaction. If there still are no appropriate stimuli, the fixed-action pattern may occur anyway. This pattern is called a *vacuum activity.*

Lorenz once proposed what has come to be known as the "flush-toilet model" of action-specific energy. As you see in Figure 4.5, Lorenz's "toilet" cannot flush unless action-specific energy has been accumulated in its tank. When the tank has filled, the appropriate key stimuli—that is, the weights on the tray—will work the releasing mechanism to discharge the "water" through pre-existing pathways. Vacuum activity can be accounted for by assuming that tank overflows can spill into the pathways. More elaborate models have been constructed to account for other phenomena, such as appetitive behavior and displacement activity.

THE "NEO-ETHOLOGISTS"

Many contemporary ethologists criticize the school of classical ethology. One of their major criticisms concerns the term "innate." The classical ethologists use this term to mean that a behavior or releasing mechanism is "inborn," "built-in," or "prewired," and that experience or interaction with the environment does not play a critical part in its development. In order to determine whether a given behavior or releasing mechanism is innate, it is considered necessary to conduct a deprivation experiment (Eibl-Eibesfeldt, 1970; Lorenz, 1965). In such an experiment, an animal typically is isolated from others of its own species at birth and is prevented from having experiences related to the behavior or releasing mechanism being studied. If, subsequently, the behavior is performed normally at its first occurrence, or if the appropriate sign stimulus releases a response on its first presentation, the classical ethologists say that the behavior or releasing mechanism is innate. However, as the neo-ethologists point out, an animal isolated from others of its species and prevented from having certain types of experience is not isolated from the rest of the environment. Other experiences—that is, other types of general or specific sensory, motor, or even neural activity—might well be critical in the development of the behavior or releasing mechanism in question. Indeed, no battery of deprivation experiments could rule out all such possibilities. Therefore,

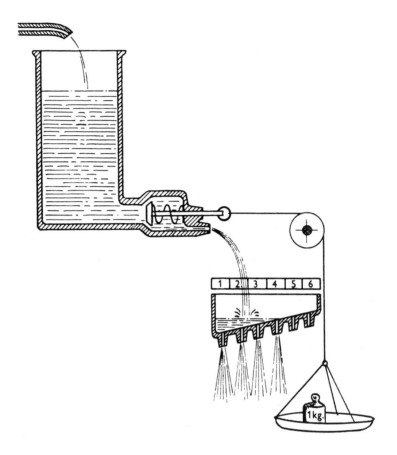

Figure 4.5

Lorenz's hydraulic model of 1950. From Lorenz, K.,
The comparative method in studying innate behaviour patterns, *Symposia of the Society for Experimental Biology,* 1950, *4,* 256. Reprinted by permission.

to say that interaction with the environment is not critical in the origin
of "innate" behavior is to make an untestable assumption. Moreover,
this assumption is incorrect insofar as an environment within some
limits is necessary for the organism to develop and survive at all; the
organism depends on a relatively normal environment in order to grow.

The importance of the deprivation experiment lies in the consequences of classifying a behavior or releasing mechanism as "innate."
The use of such a label often implies that the classical ethologist feels
that the basic nature of the phenomenon is known and that he will not

make further inquiries into its origin. This is unfortunate, for more intensive analyses of so-called "innate" responses and stimulus-response relationships can greatly improve our understanding of the development of behavior.

For all of these reasons, many modern ethologists do not use the term innate to describe a behavior. All behaviors are considered instead to represent "the result of continuous interaction between environment and inherent potentialities through development" (Hinde & Tinbergen, 1958). A behavior therefore depends on both environment and heredity, just as the area of a rectangle depends on both its length and its height.

A second criticism of the classical approach concerns the use of models in theorization. As was indicated earlier, the classical ethologists have used mechanical devices and forms of energy as models for behavioral processes. Such models perform a service in that they summarize many data in an easily understood and attractive way. However, the neo-ethologists (for example, see Hinde, 1960) have noted some important problems springing from the use of these models. One problem comes when some new data are glibly explained in terms of a model, and thus further research is not undertaken because a ready explanation exists. For instance, consider the early conceptualization of the displacement behavior that may often be seen in an animal engaged in aggression, when it is apparently under conflicting motivations to attack and to flee. The interpretation was made that, since these motivations were incompatible, their behavioral expression could become "blocked" and that then some of the motivational energy might "spark over" to activate some out-of-context behavior. This easy explanation delayed further research, which later indicated that the response that occurred as a displacement activity was in part determined by the particular stimuli present in the conflict situation. For instance, fighting turkeys may stop to drink if water is present or feed if food is available (see Hinde, 1960, 1970). Another related problem with mechanical and energy models is that they are based on simplistic and unitary systems that are inherently incapable of accounting for the complex interaction of the many factors that actually determine behavior.

RAPPROCHEMENT OF LABORATORY AND FIELD APPROACHES 5

The independent evolution of Russian psychophysiology, American animal psychology, and European classical ethology produced a remarkable result: three separate sciences of animal behavior. The first two of these sciences are not incompatible; in fact, American animal psychologists long ago adopted basic notions and procedures from their Russian counterparts and, more recently, have expressed an interest in certain problems and theoretical developments in psychophysiology. The third science of animal behavior is more difficult to relate to the other two. Classical ethology is based largely on observations in the field or under other naturalistic conditions, and its concepts are not directly interchangeable with those from the laboratories of the American animal psychologists or the Russian students of higher nervous activity. This is an unsatisfactory state of affairs; how does one relate events in the field to those in the laboratory? In the last ten years, one way of reconciling classical ethology with the two laboratory sciences has become apparent: through the notion of species-typical behavior.

DEFINITION OF SPECIES-TYPICAL BEHAVIOR

If we spend a few hours observing an active animal, certain responses and stimulus-response relationships in its behavior soon stand out. We can give these responses names and then begin to predict, from the stimuli present, how the animal is likely to be responding. For example, consider the behaviors an observer could see in a day's study of the harbor seal on isolated Sable Island, Nova Scotia. In the morning, the seals begin to come out of the sea onto the island's sandy shore (Figure 5.1). A seal may "beach" several times before it actually "hauls out." It usually beaches and hauls out near seals that are already on shore. In hauling out, a seal will typically first roll about in the sand and then move up out of the waves in a series of lumbering advances. As it advances, the new arrival will ordinarily avoid coming within a seal's length of any other animals. Should the newcomer come too close to another animal, it may be repulsed with aggressive responses such as flipper-slapping. When the seal stops its progression, it may briefly assume an alert head-up stance, looking this way and that. The seal usually then grooms and goes to sleep. This sleep will alternate with bouts of wakefulness and grooming.

Figure 5.1

Pod of harbor seals hauled out on Sable Island, Nova Scotia. Photograph by Henry James.

If a pod of seals remains undisturbed, it will grow in number until mid-afternoon and will finally break up at sundown, when the seals return to the sea to fish. Reactions to disturbances vary. If the observer makes a sudden movement, or if a tern calls, many of the seals may wake and show an alert posture, with their eyes oriented roughly in the direction of the disturbing stimulus. If there is no further movement or noise, the seals usually resume their sleep. If the disturbance persists, the seals may quickly retreat to the sea.

All these behaviors are easily seen by an observer hidden in the dunes of Sable Island. To be sure, this student of the harbor seal would need more time in the field to refine his conceptions of these behaviors and to delineate additional stimuli and responses. Yet with only a day's study, the student could gain a fair impression of how the seal behaves on land.

Many of the behaviors that may be seen in the harbor seal on Sable Island are typical of the species. That is, wherever we find harbor seals, we will see many of the same activities. This principle holds true for a great deal of the behavior we observe in the field; for example, herring gulls glide in the same fashion wherever they are found; wolves howl throughout their range. Such behavior patterns are as characteristic of

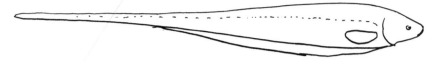

Figure 5.2

Author's sketch of a line drawing of the glass knife-fish Eigenmannia virescens. From Ellis, 1911.

species as their physical forms. Species-typical behaviors have, of course, long been emphasized in the work of the classical ethologists.

Other behaviors that we observe may not be typical of the species as a whole; rather, these behaviors may be characteristic of the animals of a region or of a particular group to which the animal belongs. One example of regionally characteristic behavior is provided by the push-up, or head-bobbing, display of the side-blotched lizard, *Uta stansburiana.* The average number and pattern of head-bobs in this display vary in different parts of the species' range (Ferguson, 1971; McKinney, 1971). An instance of group-characteristic behavior is seen in the Japanese macaque (Miyadi, 1964). Different troops of these monkeys often possess distinct food preferences. For example, eggs may be included in the diet of one troop, whereas rice may constitute a large part of another troop's fare.

Finally, some of the behaviors we observe in the field may not be typical of the species, area, or group but, instead, may be characteristic of the individual. For example, individual food specializations have been noted in rainbow, brook, and cutthroat trout (Bryan & Larkin, 1972). At least for short periods of time, these trout may specialize in capturing such prey as small fishes or snails; indeed, there is suggestive evidence that these specializations persist for months in some individuals.

In many cases, a behavior can be characteristic of both an individual and its species. For instance, nocturnal South American glass knifefishes (*Eigenmannia*) produce a constant weak electrical discharge that functions in communication and navigation (Figure 5.2). The simple wave form of this discharge is similar for all members of a species, but when an aggregation of these fish forms, each individual will then "broadcast" at a slightly different but distinctive frequency (Schwassmann, personal communication). Since this frequency is in itself one from the very narrow range that can be produced by members of the species, it is simultaneously characteristic of individual and species.

NEW APPROACHES TO SPECIES-TYPICAL BEHAVIOR

Several animal psychologists are now beginning to think about the species-typical behaviors so long discussed by the classical ethologists. These psychologists recognize that it is difficult to explain many of these species-typical behaviors in terms of conventional learning. That is, many species-typical behaviors do not appear to result from ordinary learning in the individual's lifetime. Some psychologists have suggested that, in such cases, the behaviors have arisen in the course of evolution. For example, Skinner (1966, 1969) has recently come to believe that certain species-typical behaviors have developed through evolutionary contingencies in a manner similar to the manner in which operant behavior arises from reinforcement contingencies. As a species evolves, its members produce various heritable responses; some of these responses result in an increased reproductive success for an individual and are thus "reinforced" by natural selection. The contingencies of selection can act not only on responses but also on stimulus-response relationships. The animal may have a selective advantage if it produces a given response when certain stimuli are present. In other words, these stimuli set the occasion for increased reproductive success. Selective pressure thus exists for the species to "acquire" heritable tendencies to respond when these stimuli occur.

In addition to reflecting on the origin of species-typical behaviors, psychologists are also beginning to recognize the importance of species-typical responses and stimulus-response relationships in learning. This recognition marks a great change from previous times, in which often all stimuli and all responses were regarded as equivalent for animals in a learning situation.

Complementing this new approach to species-typical behavior in animal psychology are recent studies on learning reported by zoologically trained classical ethologists and neo-ethologists. These investigations indicate that, in many cases, the structure or the stimulus control of species-typical behaviors can be modified through experience. In other words, the species-typical responses or the species-typical stimuli that lead to the responses can be changed through interaction with the environment. Such modifications may account for many of the area, group, and individual variations seen in behavior.

In this chapter, some of the new research concerning species-typical behavior will be reviewed. This research may well provide a meeting ground for many students of animal behavior and, in the future, may permit a synthesis of their theoretical concepts. The new studies can also help relate investigation in the laboratory to observation in the field.

MODIFICATION OF SPECIES-TYPICAL BEHAVIORS BY LEARNING

How can learning affect species-typical behaviors? A partial answer to this question has been provided by recent work on the ontogeny of certain species-typical behaviors (ontogeny refers to the development of behavior within the lifetime of the individual). Studies have been

Figure 5.3

Begging peck in the young laughing gull nestling.
From Hailman, J. P., The ontogeny of an instinct:
The pecking response in chicks of the laughing gull
(*Larus atricilla L.*) and related species, *Behaviour,*
1968, p. 159. Reprinted by permission.

made of the development of both single responses and response sequences, as well as of the development of stimulus control (that is, the
capacity of a stimulus to make a response more probable).

Hailman (1967, 1969) studied the development of a single species-
typical response, the begging peck of the laughing gull chick (Figure
5.3). In the older chick, the begging response is a coordinated peck at
the parent's bill, which is followed by grasping and stroking of the bill.
Preceding the grasping of the bill, the chick's head shows an anticipa-
tory rotation. Such pecks cause the parent to regurgitate food for the
young. Hailman compared the begging peck in chicks reared in the
wild with that of chicks reared by their parents in the laboratory but
deprived of the opportunity to peck. The accuracy of the chicks' aim
in pecking the bill of a stuffed gull improved with time in both experienced and deprived birds, but the experienced chicks' pecking was
more accurate. The head-rotation component of the begging peck appeared more frequently with increasing age in the experienced chicks

but was seldom observed in the deprived birds. Therefore, it is evident that experience contributes to the form of the begging peck seen in the older chick. However, experience does not in any simple way account for either the initial appearance of the peck in all chicks or the improvement in its accuracy that was observed in deprived chicks.

More complex are those cases in which the animal forms or modifies a sequence of responses that then constitutes a species-typical pattern. Eibl-Eibesfeldt (1970) has described the development of an appetitive sequence in the squirrel.

Squirrels (*Sciurus vulgaris*) possess the movements of gnawing and prying, but they must learn how to employ these behavior patterns effectively when opening a nut. Experienced squirrels can do this with a minimum of wasted effort. They gnaw a furrow on the broad side of a nut from base to tip, possibly a second one, wedge their lower incisors into the crack, and break the nut open into two halves. Inexperienced squirrels, on the other hand, gnaw without purpose, cutting random furrows until the nut breaks at one place or the other. They already try to wedge their teeth into the opening, their attempts to pry them open leading to success only if the furrows have been gnawed in the proper way. The first improvements in the technique can be seen when the furrows run parallel to the grain of the nut and are concentrated on the broad side of the nut. The squirrel follows the path of least resistance, and in this way the activity of the squirrel is guided in a specific direction by the very structure of the nut. The squirrel continues with its attempts to pry, and it keeps repeating those actions which have led to success. In this way most squirrels acquire the most efficient prying technique. . . . There are, however, individual deviations. Some squirrels learned to open nuts by gnawing a hole by a few closely spaced furrows. One squirrel achieved almost instant success by gnawing a hole into the base of the nut and continued to use this technique [pp. 210–211, references to figures in text deleted].*

These deviations remind us that learning processes that yield species-typical behavior sequences may also produce sequences characteristic of individuals.

In many cases, the stimulus control of species-typical responses in individuals can become modified through learning experiences. To cite a common example, many animals can rapidly learn to shun an aversive prey species that initially released their species-typical feeding pattern. Thus toads may quickly cease to respond to honeybees after the first few captures (Brower & Brower, 1962).

Changes in the stimulus control of species-typical responses due to learning are frequently seen in young animals. For instance, in Hailman's studies (1967, 1969) of the begging peck in gull chicks, he ob-

*From *Ethology: The Biology of Behavior,* by Irenaus Eibl-Eibesfeldt, 1970. Reprinted by permission of the publisher, Holt, Rinehart and Winston, Inc.

Figure 5.4

Begging in older herring gull chicks. Photograph by
A. R. Lock.

served the development of the chick's recognition of its parent through
the use of model gull heads. Whereas newly hatched laughing gull
chicks initially pecked at a variety of model heads, chicks taken from
the nest later in their development showed their highest rate of response to models resembling their parent's head. Interestingly, the
newly hatched chicks showed no distinctive preference between the
model heads of laughing gulls and herring gulls, although the two are
quite dissimilar in appearance. Adult laughing gulls have a black head
with a red bill, and adult herring gulls have a white head with a predom-
inately yellow bill. When newly hatched herring gull chicks were studied, they likewise showed no preference between model laughing gull
and herring gull heads. Older wild-reared herring gull chicks (see Figure 5.4) responded more frequently to the model of their parent. To
determine the role of learning in the development of this parental
recognition, Hailman reared herring gull chicks and presented food to
some when they pecked a herring gull model and to others when they
pecked a laughing gull model. In a test with both models after two days
of training, the chicks pecked more often at their training model. This
evidence shows that the herring gull chick learns some form of parental

recognition in the nest. In other words, through experience, stimuli characteristic of the parental species come to control the begging peck.

THE EFFECTS OF SPECIES-TYPICAL BEHAVIOR ON LEARNING

The preceding paragraphs have indicated that learning may generate or modify species-typical behavior. Species-typical behavior, on the other hand, may facilitate or impair learning. This conclusion has recently been reached by psychologists training animals for commercial exhibition and by psychologists working in the laboratory.

Breland and Breland have provided perhaps the most extensive account of the role of species-typical behavior in learning. The Brelands were students of Skinner who left academic life to go into the business of animal training. Using principles derived in the laboratory, they enthusiastically set about training animals to perform in county fairs, museum exhibits, and television commercials (1951). Although their business prospered, their principles soon proved to have limitations (1961, 1966). Perhaps the greatest limitation resulted from the fixity of the behavioral repertoire that the Brelands saw in many of the species that they trained. Behavior sequences were observed to range in fixity from ones that were "built-in" and that were exhibited in the same form in all members of a species to ones that showed great "flexibility" and "alterability." The repertoire of some species was largely composed of fixed sequences, and little modification could be made in these behaviors. In other species, great changes could be made in the form of behaviors by using operant-conditioning techniques.

The Brelands suggested that the "phylogenetic level"[1] and the ecological niche of a species were important in determining the flexibility of its repertoire (1966). A niche is the part of the environment that a species utilizes. Some species use only a small portion of the total environment; others exploit a larger portion. Animals lower on the "phylogenetic scale" and animals that occupied narrower niches tended to have less modifiable behavior repertoires. For example, the repertoire of the "lowly" fish is more determined and unchangeable

---

[1]Recently, the term "phylogenetic scale" has fallen into some disrepute. The concept of a phylogenetic scale has implied to many that animals can be ranked on a continuum from the "lowest" to the "highest," the highest being man. It has also been assumed that "higher" forms represent "advances" from "lower" ones and that one might expect animals from the "higher phyletic levels" to be superior in their performance to those from "lower levels." However, evolution does not proceed in the linear fashion suggested by this notion of phylogenetic scale. Rather, evolution proceeds independently and simultaneously for all living taxa. Evolution should be represented not by a scale but by a tree, each branch and twig of which symbolize evolving taxa. One cannot logically say that one taxon is higher than another or assume that all taxa can be ranked on a scale of superiority. One can study the performances of different taxa in a variety of tasks and report on the success and failure of these animals, just as did the Brelands. However, today one would not frame the conclusions of such research in terms of the phylogenetic scale (see Hodos & Campbell, 1969).

than that of the mammal, and the repertoire of the narrow-niche rabbit is more fixed than that of the broad-niche raccoon.

> The rabbit lives only on the ground, and eats only vegetable foods; the raccoon is at home on the ground, in the trees, and to some extent in the water, and is omnivorous—he will eat anything. The rabbit has relatively more invariable patterned sequences—he hops, sniffs, digs, scratches, and pulls—and very little else. The raccoon does all of these and many more; he climbs, manipulates things with his paws, "plays," and so on [p. 37].

The rabbit's species-typical behavior can be little modified; the raccoon can be taught many new tricks.

Breland and Breland primarily used reward to modify species-typical behavior. Bolles (1970) has suggested that, in situations in which animals learn to escape or avoid some aversive condition, species-typical behaviors likewise play a role in what animals can learn. Bolles believes that each animal possesses its own set of species-specific defense reactions (SSDRs). These reactions are elicited by such events as the appearance of a predator or the "sudden appearance of large innocuous objects." The SSDRs are effective in averting danger from predators and are readily evoked. According to Bolles, these responses are indeed "innate"; the animal simply does not have the opportunity to acquire defensive reactions through a slow acquisition process.

> The mouse does not scamper away from the owl because it has learned to escape the painful claws of its enemy; it scampers away from anything happening in its environment, and it does so merely because it is a mouse. The gazelle does not flee from an approaching lion because it has been bitten by lions; it runs away from any large object that approaches it, and it does so because this is one of its species-specific defense reactions. Neither the mouse nor the gazelle can afford to *learn* to avoid; survival is too urgent, the opportunity to learn is too limited, and the parameters of the situation make the necessary learning impossible [p. 33].

Even in domesticated rats, dogs, and monkeys, these SSDRs lie right beneath the surface; if the animal is shocked or otherwise presented with noxious stimuli, its "innate" defense reactions come to the fore. Indeed, the gentle domesticated creature is thus temporarily converted into a wild animal.

Avoidance learning, according to Bolles, can occur only if the avoidance response required is an SSDR. This avoidance response is acquired through the suppression of the other SSDRs. Avoidance training, in other words, is a process in which competing SSDRs drop out and only the effective SSDR remains. When the successful SSDR has a high initial probability of occurring in the situation, it may be acquired more rapidly.

For this reason, a rat can learn to jump out of a box after a single trial, or learn to run down an alley in six trials, to avoid shock. Here the SSDRs of flight have a high initial probability of occurring, and the response is thus rapidly acquired. On the other hand, rats have more difficulty in learning to spin cylinders or to press bars in order to avoid shock; in fact, some never learn in these situations. Bolles feels that these difficult responses are learned when the animal somehow succeeds in getting one of its SSDRs to satisfy the avoidance requirements. For example, in order to barpress, the rat must learn to "freeze" at the bar in such a fashion that it is depressed, thus engaging in a defense mechanism that serves at the same time as a learned activity.

Many other psychologists (for example, Seligman, 1970; Shettleworth, 1972) are now concerned with the role of species-typical behaviors in learning. Increased understanding of this role should clarify the relationship between results from the psychology laboratory and observations of learning in the field.

SPECIES-TYPICAL LEARNING MECHANISMS

As we have seen, species-typical behaviors may constrain, facilitate, or be the product of learning. A learning ability is also species-typical. It evolves like any species characteristic: the individuals that possess some distinctive and beneficial learning capacity have a selective advantage over their fellows; their increased reproductive potential means that this trait will tend to be acquired by the species. The learning mechanism acquired by a species may "teach" only a few behaviors, or it may have more general effects. The learning mechanism may be unique to the species, or similar mechanisms may be found in many species. The learning mechanism often involves the interaction of several different processes.

For example, consider the learning that may be involved in the development of birdsong (see Hinde, 1970; Thorpe, 1958, 1961). In many species, birdsong is passed on by each generation to the next. However, the "pupils" may be selective in what they learn. For instance, the chaffinch male sings from one to six distinct "full" songs, which all conform to a common pattern. These songs all last from two to three seconds, range from 1500 to 8000 Hz, and consist of three phrases followed by a "terminal flourish" (see Figure 5.5). Species-typical adult song develops from subsong, which has an irregular number of notes and a variable duration. Birds taken from the nest at a few days of age do not develop species-typical song; they produce a "simple" song of approximately the right duration but without the phrases or flourishes proper to the full song. In contrast, chaffinches captured

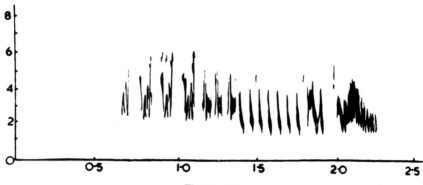

Figure 5.5

Chaffinch normal song. The vertical axis in the sono-
gram indicates frequency in kilohertz (KHz); the
horizontal axis represents time in seconds. From
Thorpe, W. H., The learning of song patterns of birds
with especial reference to the song of the chaffinch
(*Fringilla coelebs*), *Ibis,* 1958, *100,* 535–570. Reprinted by permission.

during their first fall and then isolated from other birds develop "more
or less" normal song. Almost-normal song is also produced by birds
taken early from the nest but exposed to recordings of chaffinch song
in fall. These facts indicate that chaffinches learn their adult song before
they sing it in the spring. Chaffinches cannot learn just any song, however. If one performs the experiment of playing an artificial song with
a flutelike quality to birds isolated early from other chaffinches, no
modification will be heard in the simple song they develop as adults. If,
instead, one plays a distorted rendition of a chaffinch song—for example, if one plays it backward—the isolates later modify their song, and
some may produce a nearly perfect imitation.

The species-typical song can have reinforcing properties. For example, males captured in the fall and injected with the reproductive
hormone testosterone will learn to land on a bar to hear species-typical
song. Untreated autumn-captured males and testosterone-injected isolates show a lower rate of response; untreated isolates do not learn. Song
not only is reinforcing but also has a releasing function: in the field,
chaffinches often sing in response to each other's songs. Moreover, if
one plays songs to individual chaffinches, the song type that best releases its singing is the one most frequently sung by the individual.

Putting this evidence together, Hinde (1970) suggests that perhaps
the bird possesses a crude model of the species-typical song that is
"improved by the experience of the song." During this process of improvement, sounds that approximate the model act both as reinforcers
and as eliciting stimuli for song.

Many animals possess more general learning mechanisms—mechanisms that can teach the animals many new behaviors in a variety of stimulus situations. For example, operant conditioning occurs in many species. Another widespread learning mechanism has been described by Garcia and his associates (Garcia, McGowan, & Green, 1972). This mechanism was first observed in investigations of radiation-produced taste aversion in rats. These rats reduced their intake of distinctively flavored water that had been associated with low-level X-radiation. Such radiation produces toxicosis in the rats—that is, it makes them "sick." The rats thus learned to avoid drinking a distinctively flavored liquid that had been present when they became ill. Further experimentation revealed that this conditioned aversion could develop even if the radiation onset were delayed until hours after the rat had tasted a flavored liquid. That aversions could develop after such a long delay was unexpected on the basis of other work in learning. A second finding was also unpredicted: although the rats could learn to avoid a flavored liquid, they could not learn to avoid liquids that were associated with distinctive sounds and visual stimuli. In a well-known experiment, it was shown that rats made ill would reduce their intake of flavored water that was associated with the onset of their illness, but that, under similar conditions, they would not learn to avoid "noisy, bright" water, water that had been accompanied by sound and light whenever it was consumed. However, when rats were given a shock to their paws for drinking, they would not come to avoid the flavored water, but they would reduce their intake of noisy, bright water (Figure 5.6).

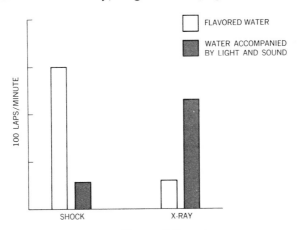

Figure 5.6

Reduction in consumption of flavored and noisy, bright water following shock or X-radiation. After Garcia, J., & Koelling, R. A., Relation of cue to consequence in avoidance learning, *Psychonomic Science,* 1966, *4,* 123–124. Used by permission.

Conditioned aversions have now been demonstrated in several other mammals, including mice, cats, and primates. Aversions may be developed to a variety of foods, including laboratory chow, chocolate, milk, and alcohol. A number of methods for creating toxicosis can produce these effects (see Revusky & Garcia, 1970). Evidence indicates that such conditioned aversions can be important in the field as well as in the laboratory. For example, wild rats that survive eating poisoned food will subsequently avoid the food but will not avoid the place where they took the bait (see Garcia, McGowan, & Green, 1972).

All this evidence led Garcia and his colleagues to the conclusion that a special learning process exists for taste aversion.

Natural selection has designed the rat with ... another system to cope with the internal environment. Foodstuffs are chemically analyzed by gustatory and olfactory receptors when sniffed and eaten. Later, as the food is absorbed, internal receptors report on the ultimate effects within the internal environment. These two afferent categories converge upon a visceral [integration] center which is relatively insulated from stimuli arising in the external environment. Since food absorption takes time, this system has become specialized to handle long interstimulus intervals [p. 22].

It should be noted that Garcia's view has not been accepted by all. For example, Revusky (1971) believes that the same learning principles can account for the acquisition of both taste aversions and more orthodox forms of avoidance responses. He explains the differences in their development by the assumption that particular kinds of psychological events have "relevance" for one another. That is, certain classes of stimuli, responses, and reinforcements can be easily associated with each other but not with other types of psychological events. Using the principle of relevance, Revusky argues that taste-toxicosis associations are learned in a single trial, even over long delays, because (1) taste stimuli and illness are readily associated, (2) other classes of events are not readily associated with taste stimuli and illness, and (3) those tastes that occur in the interval between the typically novel test stimulus and the illness are familiar and few and thus do not provide enough associative interference to prevent the acquisition of the avoidance response.

In any case, this controversy indicates that, although one may speak of mechanisms that teach animals specific behaviors, it is not always an easy task to discover which underlying learning processes are at work in the situation. Indeed, the description of such processes has been the goal of animal psychologists for decades. Many types of modification in behavior are discussed in this book. Although it would be difficult to suggest one or two simple principles that account for all of these types of learning, it should be apparent that certain learning processes operate widely.

PHYSIOLOGICAL BASES OF SPECIES-TYPICAL BEHAVIOR

Classical ethologists have long expressed interest in the neural bases of species-typical behavior. For example, in 1951, Tinbergen enthusiastically cited the work of W. R. Hess and his colleagues in the 1940s. Hess's pioneering research demonstrated that brief electrical stimulations of areas in the brain of the cat could elicit the species-typical behavior patterns involved in fighting, sleeping, or eating (see Hess, 1957). These patterns included typical appetitive sequences; for example, the cat searched for a corner before going to sleep.

The classical ethologists' concern about the neural bases of species-typical behaviors has come to be shared by several physiological psychologists. Part of this recent interest had its origin in the remarkable discovery by Olds and Milner in 1954 of a new kind of reward: rats readily learned to go to a place or to press a bar to receive a brief electrical stimulation in their brain. The effects of stimulation at certain brain sites could be quite striking: hungry rats would ignore food to stimulate themselves; rates of over 5000 responses an hour could be obtained; rats would self-stimulate until they dropped from exhaustion (Olds, 1956, 1958).

Subsequently, it became clear that brain stimulation can do more than reinforce responses such as pressing a bar; it can directly elicit species-typical behaviors. This was most compellingly demonstrated in the case of feeding the rat. It was known that electrical stimulation of certain points in the lateral hypothalamus of a rat's brain could cause a satiated animal to feed. In 1962, two studies (Hoebel & Teitelbaum; Margules & Olds) independently showed that rats would learn to bar-press for stimulation at the same brain sites where feeding responses could be elicited. Around this time and subsequently, several other studies reported that sexual behavior, gnawing, nest building, and aggressive responses could be elicited by stimulation of the same neural structures that had been shown to yield high rates of self-stimulation.

In 1967, Glickman and Schiff reviewed the relationship of brain stimulation to reward and species-typical behaviors. Species-typical behavior sequences were classified as involving either approach or withdrawal. Approach sequences included responses seen in exploration, feeding, drinking, sex, maternal care, grooming, predation, and, probably, territorial defense. Withdrawal behaviors included escape from a highly aversive stimulus, fleeing a predator, and other, less dramatic, responses. Stimulation at positive brain sites—that is, areas where stimulation was rewarding—could produce approach movements and, if proper stimulus support was present, often released species-typical approach behavior. Brain stimulation at negative sites, where stimulation was escaped or avoided, tended to produce backward movements, freezing, or other fear responses. Glickman and Schiff concluded that the expression of species-typical behavior patterns normally constitutes reward or punishment. Rewarding or punishing brain stimulation could short-circuit such behavioral expression by directly facilitating activity in the neural sites controlling species-typical behaviors. It should be noted that the notion that species-typical behavior is critical in reward or punishment is not new (for example, see Lorenz, 1937b; Sheffield, 1954). What is new is the specification of the relationship between intracranial stimulation effects and species-typical behaviors.

The theorization and experimentation reviewed in this chapter illustrate the increasing resemblance between the interests and concepts of many animal psychologists and those of zoologically oriented students of animal behavior. This new communality of spirit should yield many benefits for the study of animal behavior.

RESEARCH AREAS IN ANIMAL BEHAVIOR

PART 2

The first part of this book traced the development of three contemporary traditions in the study of animal behavior. In Russia, the study of higher nervous activity grew out of the physiological laboratory. In Europe, ethology was evolved by zoologists working under naturalistic conditions. In North America, behavioristic animal psychology was created by psychologists who lost their mentalism in the puzzle box, maze, and kindred apparatus. With the exception of the American adoption of several concepts from Pavlov and Bekhterev, the schools remained relatively isolated until the middle 1950s. Since that time, communication has become more frequent among some workers in the major traditions. The new approaches discussed in Chapter 5 reflect this increasing interchange.

At this point, it should be stressed that there are a great number of animal behaviorists who do not identify themselves with any of these major schools. Many of them study animal behavior from the perspective of ecology, anthropology, primatology, or ornithology. Their special interests include such topics as socioecology or the evolution of primate behavior. Their work forms part of the diversity of theory and research that characterizes the study of animal behavior.

The second part of this book will consider the contributions of those people who work both within and independently of the major schools through a survey of several contemporary areas in animal behavior. The areas—exploration and fear, behavioral rhythms, vertebrate social behavior, socialization, and primate behavior—will illustrate how much we have recently learned and how much we still need to know. These are exciting times in the study of animal behavior: the breadth and depth of our knowledge increase continuously, for our science is characterized by expansion and change.

Although the areas treated here are only a sample, they were selected to bear on the four major questions that can be asked in studying animal behavior (see Hinde, 1970, Chapter 1; Tinbergen, 1963). The first question is that of the *mechanism* or *immediate causes* of behavior. This question inquires into the events that immediately precede a given behavior. The question may take such forms as: What are the stimuli that control this behavior? What are the neural and physiological bases for the behavior?

The second question deals with *ontogeny,* or the development of behavior in the individual. One might ask: What is the course of development of a given behavior in the organism's lifetime? How is the development of the behavior affected by environmental or organismic factors?

The third question concerns the *adaptive function* of behavior. What functions does a particular behavior serve? How does the behavior adapt the animal to its environment?

The fourth question is that of the *evolution* of behavior. How did some pattern of behavior evolve? How did the ancestral forms of a contemporary taxon behave? In what manner were the responses of a contemporary taxon derived from those of its predecessors?

In the conclusions to the remaining chapters, we will consider how each research area represents the animal behaviorists' approach to one of these fundamental questions.

EXPLORATION AND FEAR

6

Exploratory behavior is characteristic of the higher vertebrates. Consider the behaviors of the rhesus monkey.

Monkeys, not unlike children, persist in examining things in their immediate environment by close inspection and manipulation. Every object presented to a monkey is at one time or another handled, fondled, scratched, rubbed, bent, picked at, bitten and pulled apart before finally being discarded. A monkey will tamper with the lock in his cage door and will invariably confiscate any objects left on accessible shelves [Butler, 1954, p. 70].

Another description of exploration is that of the raven's behavior.

A young Raven, confronted with a new object (which may be a camera, an old bottle, a stuffed polecat or anything else), first reacts with escape responses. He will fly up to an elevated perch and, from this point of vantage, stare at the object literally for hours. After this, he will begin to approach the object very gradually, maintaining all the while a maximum of caution and the expressive attitude of intense fear. He will cover the last distance from the object hopping sideways, with half-raised wings, in the utmost readiness to flee. At last, he will deliver a single fearful blow with his powerful beak at the object and forthwith fly back to his safe perch. If nothing happens he will repeat the same procedure in much quicker sequence and with more confidence. If the object is an animal that flees the Raven loses all fear in a fraction of a second and will start in pursuit instantly. If it is an animal that charges he will either try to get behind it and tease it by trying to repeat the attack or, if the charge is sufficiently impressive, loses interest in a very short time. With an inanimate object, the Raven will proceed to apply a number of further instinctive movements. He will grab it with one foot, peck at it, try to tear off pieces, insert his bill into any existing cleft and then pry apart his mandible with considerable force. Finally, if the object is not too big, the Raven will carry it away, push it into a convenient hole and cover it with some inconspicuous material [Lorenz, 1956, p. 636].*

One definition of exploratory behavior is that it comprises all responses made to produce stimulus changes that have no direct significance to the animal's survival. In other words, exploration produces

*From Lorenz, K., *L'Instinct dans le Comportement des Animaux et de l'Homme*, 1956. Reprinted by permission of the publisher, Masson et Cie, Paris.

stimuli that do not signal food, predator, mate, or any other condition of immediate importance to the animal's well-being. These stimuli tend to be novel, complex, moderately intense, or varying.

How prominent is exploratory behavior in most species? One extensive study provides a partial answer to this question. Using the facilities of the Lincoln Park and Bronx Zoos, Glickman and Sroges (1966) studied the exploratory behavior of 200 animals representing more than 100 species. All animals were subjected to the same experimental procedure. They were presented a series of novel objects, either in their home cage or in an adjacent familiar cage. The stimulus objects included a pair of wooden blocks, two dowels, two pieces of rubber hose, two steel chains, and a ball of crumpled paper. The objects in each pair were of different dimensions and were selected to be of an appropriate size for the animal. Each stimulus or stimulus pair was placed in the animal's cage and then removed after 6 minutes, and there was a 5- to 20-minute interstimulus rest period. The 6-minute period, in which each kind of object was in the cage, was divided into 5-second periods. Two types of behaviors were counted during the 5-second periods. One was a contact response, in which the animal actually made contact with the stimulus. The other was an orientation response, in which the animal turned toward the stimulus. A total response score was computed for each animal by summing the scores for contact and orientation responses.

Clear differences in exploratory behaviors were seen among the major taxonomic divisions. Primates and carnivores exhibited more exploratory behavior than rodents, a group of "primitive" mammals, and reptiles. There was no statistically significant difference between primates and carnivores or between rodents and primitive mammal groups in terms of contact and total-response scores. However, there was a difference in orientation scores. Primates showed significantly more orientation responses than carnivores, and carnivores showed more than rodents, primitive mammals, and reptiles. Rodents, primitive mammals, and reptiles emitted so few orientation responses that comparisons among them were not meaningful.

No systematic sex differences were observed in responses within the main taxonomic divisions. As might be expected, in species for which comparisons could be made, subadults tended to show higher response scores than adults. There also appeared to be a shift in the mode of exploration between subadults and adults, such that adult animals gave a greater percentage of orienting reactions. For all of the main taxonomic categories, the average number of responses to the novel objects declined over the course of the test sessions.

Of great importance is the fact that different groups showed species-typical behavior patterns. For example:

The typical primate within our sample approached an object within the first minute, after an initial orienting response, picked it up in the forepaws, and chewed on it, stopping at various points to sniff it or to inspect it visually while turning the object about in the forepaws. . . . Such behaviour was exhibited by 70% of the primate sample. . . . An additional 15% touched or sniffed the objects briefly without ever biting them, while 11% of the sample demonstrated only [observing] responses [Glickman & Sroges, 1966, p. 164].

The distinguishing characteristics of primate exploration, as contrasted with that of the other groups, were these visual and manipulatory responses. Another notable characteristic observed in primates was a low level of fear responses in adult animals.

The carnivores showed behavior patterns rather similar to some of those found in their normal predatory activities.

In terms of qualitative response patterns, mouthing or chewing responses dominated behavior. However, the group generally produced an unusually high percentage of the kind of vigorous swatting, chasing, "worrying" activities which are generally classed as "playful". . . . The mobile paws of the Felidae and Canidae were extensively used for batting objects about the cage [p. 171].

One can recognize these felid and canid behaviors immediately if one sees some of Glickman's films (see Figure 6.1). The lions and tigers, for example, act just like kittens playing with balls of yarn.

The rodents, of special interest to psychologists, were quite variable in the quantity of exploratory behavior they showed. The hystricomorphs, which include porcupines and agoutis, were the most reactive. The sciuromorphs, which include squirrels and marmots, were intermediate in response. The myomorphs, the mouselike rodents, showed hardly any responses.

With the exception of a single Orinoco crocodile, which acted almost like one of the carnivores, the reptiles were very unreactive. The most frequent response score in this class was zero.

THE TAXONOMY AND TOPOGRAPHY OF EXPLORATORY BEHAVIOR

As is evident from a consideration of the work of Glickman and Sroges, there are many responses that may be considered exploratory behaviors. Although the merits of any classificatory scheme are somewhat moot, one system that may be useful is the one drawn up by Berlyne (1960). When an exploratory response consists of changes in posture and/or in the orientation of sense organs, it can be called an *orienting response*. When the exploratory response consists of locomo-

Figure 6.1

Exploration in the snow leopard. From Glickman, S.
E., & Sroges, R. W., Curiosity in zoo animals, *Behaviour*, 1966, *26*, 151–188. Reprinted by permission.

tion, it can be called *locomotor exploration.* When the exploratory response causes changes in external objects, it can be called an *investigatory response.*

ORIENTING RESPONSES

Much of the information available concerning orienting behavior originates in the recent work of students of higher nervous activity in Russia. Sokolov (1958, 1960), Berlyne (1960, 1963), and Lynn (1966), drawing on this work, have formulated general descriptions of the orienting response or reflex. The reflex is the first response of the organism to nonpainful novel stimuli; it should be distinguished from the complex chains of exploratory responses that may follow it. The orienting reflex has many elements: it involves motor components such as shifting the eyes, turning the body, and sniffing; autonomic components such as pupil dilation, changes in breathing, and changes in the galvanic skin response, GSR (a brief drop in skin resistance); and central nervous system components such as changes in the electrical wave patterns of the brain. Many of these components may be regarded as contributing directly or indirectly to the sensitivity of perceptual systems. Many of the changes occurring have also been thought to be indicative of increased excitement, or *arousal.*

The orienting reflex changes with successive presentations of the novel stimulus. The particular change it undergoes, however, depends upon the type and intensity of the stimulus. Sokolov (1958, 1960) offers an interesting discussion of the extinction and transformation of the reflex based on studies of the reactions of human blood vessels to mild electric shock to the skin. In these studies, a second reflex could be elicited—the defensive reflex. The defensive reflex contrasts with the orienting reflex in that the former is a system for limiting the action of the stimulus rather than for enhancing its effect. The orienting reflex was indicated by a reciprocal reaction—vasoconstriction (constriction of the blood vessels) in the hands and vasodilation (dilation of the vessels) in the head—and the defensive reflex was indicated by vasoconstriction at both sites. When higher intensities of shock were presented, a defensive reflex appeared initially and persisted during subsequent trials. Somewhat lower intensities of shock elicited an initial orienting response that was replaced in later trials with a persistent defensive reflex. Still lower intensities of shock elicited only an initial orienting reflex; with these stimuli, the orienting reflex was greater in extent and frequency the more intense the stimulation.

LOCOMOTOR EXPLORATION

Locomotion in a novel maze has been considered to represent exploration (for example, Halliday, 1966; Montgomery, 1951). Such locomotion may (for example, Carr & Williams, 1957; Williams & Kuchta, 1957) or may not (for example, Halliday, 1967a, 1967b; Montgomery, 1952) exhibit intertrial decrease. Intratrial decreases, however, are commonly noted (for example, Halliday, 1967a; Montgomery, 1951). Halliday (1966) has related fear or "emotional arousal" to this locomotion. One argument for his view is that there is a rough positive relationship between autonomic activity levels and such locomotion.

The difficulty in formulating any hypothesis about the relationship of fear or arousal to locomotor exploration lies in the uncertain significance of the locomotion observed. In the first place, nonlocomotion can sometimes be regarded as more exploratory than locomotion—that is, as producing more stimulus change. For example, the animal sampling a completely new environment from a stationary position may be perceiving more stimulus change than the animal rushing helter-skelter through it. Or, as Zimbardo and Miller (1958) have theorized, the tendency to explore any novel stimulation may have to be extinguished before the animal moves on to the next novel stimulus. Again, a moving animal would not necessarily be exhibiting so strong an exploratory tendency as would a stationary one. A second problem in interpretation rests on the possibility that the locomotion may represent not behavior

functioning to produce stimulus change but, rather, behavior functioning to reduce stimulus change—that is, to produce the familiar and to
escape the novelty of the environment. Some experimental support for
the hypothesis that at least some of the locomotion represents escape
behavior has been offered by Johnston (1964).

The problem of interpretation is at least reduced when one considers locomotion that represents approach toward an object without ecological significance, or investigatory behavior that involves more
intimate contact with or stimulation from such an object. Clearly,
stimulus change is produced through the animal's behavior. Studies of
arousal or fear indices during approach and investigatory behavior
would be of extreme value in helping us sort out the relationship between fear and exploration.

INVESTIGATORY BEHAVIOR

In investigatory behavior, animals make alterations in the object
being explored. Examples of investigatory behavior, cited earlier, include the raven's treatment of novel stimuli such as cameras, the monkey's tampering with locks, and the rodent's gnawing of new blocks of
wood introduced into its cage. In these cases, investigation is direct; the
animal approaches and directly alters the stimulus. There is also an
indirect form of investigatory behavior, in which the animal makes a
change in a relatively familiar or simple stimulus in order to produce
another stimulus that is novel or complex or has some particular quality.
For instance, an animal may engage in activities such as moving an
obstacle or barpressing in order to indirectly produce some contingent
stimulus change.

Research on indirect exploratory behavior has been conducted
largely in the operant tradition and, within this tradition, the term
sensory reinforcement is used to describe the production of stimulus
changes. In some of the first studies on sensory reinforcement, in the
early 1950s, Girdner (1953) demonstrated that merely making the appearance of a small light contingent on a barpress would increase barpress rate to above base rate. Since these studies were conducted, there
has been vigorous examination of this phenomenon in mammals (Kish,
1966). However, little operant work with nonmammalian animals has
been reported.

In mammals, sensory reinforcement is possible in most sensory
modalities: effects have been found in vision, audition, kinesthesis, gus-
tation, olfaction, and touch (see Kish, 1966). The intensity and quality
of the stimulus may be critical for the production of this effect. For
example, in rats, reinforcement by light depends on the intensity of the
contingent light. Whereas moderately intense light is rewarding, extremely bright light is aversive, and very dim light has no reinforcing
properties. Work with sound reinforcement in mice illustrates the im-

portance of sensory quality: sound reinforcement occurs with low-intensity, low-frequency pure tones but not with high-intensity or high-frequency pure tones or with "white noise" (a mixture of sound waves extending over a broad frequency range) (Barnes & Kish, 1961).

PLAY

Since play involves the production of stimulus change, it may perhaps be viewed as a class of exploratory behavior. But, although there frequently may be consensus on whether or not a given behavior represents play, it is hard to set general criteria for including behaviors in the class of play. Play does seem to be more complex than other exploratory behaviors, and it also involves out-of-context species-typical behaviors. Consider the following description of the play of juvenile polecats.

Aggressive play in the young polecat is initiated by an attacker which jumps on the back of its opponent and bites it on the back of the neck. ... The opponent rolls over onto its back and makes a series of snapping bites at the muzzle and neck of its attacker, at the same time pushing it away with its paws. In response to this, the attacker either stands above its opponent and snaps its jaws in a playful attempt to bite its neck or alternatively rolls on its back, and the two animals exchange their roles of aggressor and defender. If the animals become very excited, the aggressor shakes its opponent vigorously by the neck and may drag it around the arena by the scruff of its neck. Sometimes both animals lie side by side on their backs, snapping their jaws at one another and waving their legs in the air [Poole, 1966, pp. 25–27].*

And consider the stalking play of young lion cubs: one cub will stalk another, prepare to attack, attack, and then give chase if the other cub shows play-flight (Schenkel, 1966). These examples indicate that play can involve elements of aggressive and predatory behaviors: the young polecats show behavior that later forms part of adult intraspecific aggression; the cubs' play resembles a mature animal's hunting behavior. Out-of-context elements from other species-typical behaviors—for example, from sexual or exploratory behavior—appear in play. Loizos (1966) has attempted to summarize the ways in which out-of-context behavior sequences are modified in play:

1. The sequence may be *reordered.*
2. The individual movements making up the sequence may become *exaggerated.*
3. Certain movements within the sequence may be *repeated* more than they would usually be.
4. The sequence may be broken off altogether by the introduction of irrelevant activities, and resumed later. This could be called *fragmentation.*

*From Poole, T. B. Aggressive play in polecats, *Symposium of the Zoological Society of London,* 1966, *18,* 23–44. Reprinted by permission.

5. Movements may be both *exaggerated and repeated.*
6. Individual movements within the sequence may never be completed, and this incomplete element may be repeated many times. This applies equally to both the beginning of a movement (the *intention element*) and to its ending (the *completion element*).

Furthermore:

In every case, during play, the performance of the movements from which play is derived is uneconomical, and therefore would be inefficient in terms of the original motivating context [Loizos, 1966, p. 7].

Not all elements in play derive from other behavioral contexts. In the red deer of Scotland, for instance, as Darling (1937) observed, calves engage in activities similar to the human games king-of-the-mountain and tag, as well as in mock fighting. Although the behaviors constituting king-of-the-mountain and mock fighting resemble those of adult stags when they maintain a harem in rutting season, the tag behavior has elements not seen in any other context. Interestingly, it persists as the calves mature; hinds, yearlings, and 2-year-olds may engage in ordinary tag or in the more elaborate tag that is played around a hillock. This latter kind of play involves rapid reversals in course and momentary loss of visual contact.

Two other characteristics of play have been suggested in the preceding paragraphs. First, play occurs primarily in immature animals, although it also may occur in adults. Second, the stimulus controlling play often would be inappropriate for the behavior if it appeared in context. For example, in mongooses, cats, and foxes, a stimulus normally inadequate for evoking hunting behavior, such as a companion's tail or a stone or a leaf, may cause the animal to play predator (Marler & Hamilton, 1966).

MONOTONY

As we have seen, animals engage in exploratory behavior in order to produce stimulus change. This action makes sense if the exploratory behavior brings the animal into contact with potential food sources, hiding places, and so forth, or allows the animal to become more proficient at species-typical behaviors. However, an animal's motivation for stimulus change may stem, in part at least, from another factor—monotony.

Short-term monotony. The effects of short-term monotony have been studied primarily in humans. One of the first studies made derived from a problem encountered during World War II: British radar operators were failing to detect German submarines during antisubmarine patrols. Mackworth (see Heron, 1957) studied this problem for the Royal Air Force and discovered that, within only a half hour, deterioration appeared in subjects' performance on a monotonous detection task.

In 1951, D. O. Hebb began to systematically study the effects of restricted stimulation on humans (summarized in Heron, 1957). Hebb and his collaborators created an extremely monotonous situation. His subjects rested on a bed in a constantly lighted room; they wore cotton gloves and rigid paper cuffs to reduce tactual stimulation; translucent visors eliminated their patterned visual stimulation; and their heads were placed on U-shaped foam pillows that covered their ears and attenuated the repetitious hum of air-conditioning equipment. The results of this sensory restriction were dramatic. The subjects' performance on a battery of tests was poorer than that of controls; they tended to become susceptible to an argument in favor of the existence of supernatural phenomena, some subjects remaining afraid of seeing ghosts for days after the experiment; the subjects reported that they had trouble thinking normally; and they began to hallucinate. The reports of visions, such as of "processions of squirrels with sacks over their shoulders marching purposefully" across the visual field, and of other hallucinations, were perhaps the most striking results of Hebb's study. Such experiences can also occur outside the laboratory. Arctic explorers and sailors adrift at sea on small boats report similar experiences. For example, Sir Joshua Slocum, who sailed alone around the world, reported that once, when he became ill, the pilot of Columbus' ship *Pinta* took the helm for him.

The import of the experimentation on the effects of short-term monotony is that, in humans, stimulus change is necessary to maintain normal cognitive functioning, and that the lack of stimulus change is aversive. By implication, humans may sometimes explore in order to avoid monotony. The same may hold true for other taxa. For example, a visually isolated rhesus monkey will persist for hours in repeatedly opening a door that permits a brief view of a laboratory (Butler, 1954). Perhaps this behavior is not motivated by curiosity, which was Butler's explanation, but rather by monotony.

Long-term monotony. It is clear that long-term sensory deprivation can produce severe consequences. Of particular interest are the effects of long-term deprivation on exploratory behavior and on fear responses. In monkeys and chimpanzees, monotonous rearing conditions appear to reduce exploratory behavior. In monkeys, these conditions enhance fear responses to relatively novel or relatively complex stimuli (see Mason & Green, 1962; Menzel, Davenport, & Rogers, 1963; Sackett, 1965).

Another effect of long-term monotony is the induction of stereotypic behaviors. Animals frequently show these stereotypic patterns in laboratories and old-fashioned zoos, since barren cages and small walled enclosures constitute basically monotonous environments. For example, repetitive locomotion is common in these situations. Typically, the animal repeatedly moves over some simple route. Especially common are patterns in which the animal moves in a figure eight, in a circle, or in a straight line (Hediger, 1950).

One theory of such stereotypes is that they provide a source of exteroceptive (coming from outside the organism) and proprioceptive (coming from within the organism) stimulation for an animal in a monotonous environment (Hinde, 1970). Consistent with this view are the following observations. In chimpanzees, animals that have been reared in impoverished environments develop stereotypes that do not appear in wild-caught individuals. In rhesus monkeys, stereotypes occur less frequently in the monkeys placed in larger cages. In canaries, stereotypic behavior is reduced when the birds can interact with others of their species.

Stereotyped behavior also occurs in situations that are the converse of monotony: novel or fearful stimuli can increase the rate of emission of stereotyped behaviors (see Hinde, 1970). It has been suggested that stereotypes function in these cases to reduce anxiety or to attenuate excessive stimulation.

EXPLORATORY BEHAVIOR AND FEAR RESPONSES

As is evident from the preceding discussion, certain stimulus characteristics are important in the control of exploratory behavior. Stimuli that are relatively novel, complex, and/or intense evoke exploratory behavior of the orienting, locomotor, or investigatory variety. However, it should be stressed that stimuli that are too novel, too complex, or too intense may evoke escape or avoidance rather than exploration. For example, consider the chaffinch's reaction to stimuli differing in novelty and intensity (see Hinde, 1954; Marler, 1956a). "Strong, unusual stimuli," such as an abrupt, loud noise or the cessation of a customary sound, evoke a freezing reaction. In contrast, milder stimuli, such as the appearance of a blind in an unfamiliar place or the fall of a dead branch, release "inquisitive" behavior.

The chaffinch gives a subjective impression of curiosity. . . . With crest raised and the neck rather extended . . . the bird examines the strange objects first with one eye then the other, turning quickly from side to side. The body feathers tend to be sleek and the wing-flashes may be partly concealed. Making constant restless movements, bowing and pivoting of the body on one spot, [with] flicks of the tail and rarely of the wings, the bird approaches and moves away from the object, tending to keep at some distance [Marler, 1956a, p. 19].

It should be noted that this exploration includes elements associated with flight, such as tail-flipping and crest-raising; in fact, much of the chaffinch's behavior described here is characterized by a rapid alternation of responses representing approach and withdrawal. Similar but more intense behavior is evoked by a real predator, such as a perched hawk; *mobbing* is the term employed for this common reaction of birds to predators.

The facts that the same stimulus dimensions can evoke either exploratory or fearful behavior and that exploration and fear can occur in quick succession suggest that there is a close link between these two apparently opposite types of response. One common theoretical notion concerning this link rests on the concept of arousal. According to this view, the imposition of strong stimuli on an organism causes a great increase in its state of physiological arousal. Fearful behaviors are associated with this state of high activation or excitement. Moderate increases in arousal are the result of exposure to stimuli possessing intermediate degrees of novelty, complexity, and intensity; these changes in arousal are rewarding and can motivate exploratory behavior. There are several other hypotheses about the relationship among fear, arousal, and exploration. One, mentioned earlier, related fear to locomotor exploration.

Although the nature of the underlying mechanisms relating exploration to fear is still a matter of dispute, it is interesting to note that these behaviors also share a partial resemblance in their form. As we shall see, fear, like exploration, can involve freezing behavior, locomotion, or approach characterized by intensive interaction.

THE TAXONOMY AND TOPOGRAPHY OF FEAR

As in the case of exploration, many behaviors are subsumed under the rubric of fear. Perhaps a threefold classification is also workable here, although any classification must be speculative in this stage of our knowledge. Following some of the distinctions shown in the literature (see Bolles, 1970; Driver & Humphries, 1966; Hogan, 1965, 1966), we shall distinguish immobility, retreat, and counterattack responses and discuss them in turn.

IMMOBILITY RESPONSES

Immobility responses are widespread in the animal kingdom. There is much variation in these responses. For example, they differ tremendously in their duration; some are momentary, like the human startle response, and some are long-lasting, like the spruce grouse's freezing response. The responses may also vary in the time of their occurrence: immobility may be the immediate response to a stimulus, or it may follow some other behavior, such as locomotion. Both of these patterns of behavior are seen in the paradise fish when it is introduced into an aquarium.

An unusual form of the immobility response is sometimes called *animal hypnosis* (Draper & Klemm, 1967; Gilman & Marcuse, 1949; Ratner & Thompson, 1960). This immobility reaction, produced by manual restraint, consists of the animal's remaining motionless after it has been released (see Figure 6.2). The reaction can last up to an hour; in this state, an animal may show reduced sensitivity to painful stimuli. Animal hypnosis occurs over a broad phylogenetic range, appearing, for example, in cockroaches, rays, frogs, lizards, and domestic fowl. Parallels exist between the reaction and the human hypnotic state (Draper & Klemm, 1967).

Figure 6.2

Animal hypnosis. This 3-week-old chick was restrained for 15 seconds. Following release, it remained in this position for 48 seconds. Author's photo.

Immobility responses may be the characteristic fear reaction in certain taxa or in certain age classes within a taxon. Helpless newborn fawns remain immobile at the approach of a large predator; however, as they become less helpless, they drop this behavior. Throughout their lives, guinea pigs respond to predators by freezing.

RETREAT RESPONSES

Retreat, like immobility, is a common fear reaction in the animal kingdom; and, like immobility, retreat may be too extensive a category to be useful for the student of animal behavior. Retreat reactions vary in many dimensions. Retreat may be easy or difficult to elicit; the wood duck takes flight at a very slight disturbance, whereas the woodcock flies only at the last moment. Retreat may be directed toward some point of safety, such as in the response of many grassland sparrows in taking cover from a flying predator; or it may be almost directionless, as in the jerky, rapid swimming of many bony fishes when a hand is moved over the top of an aquarium. Retreat may be brief or sustained: after a sudden vibration, a grass spider may run briefly and then remain immobile; a herd of red deer may move a great distance to avoid a stalker.

Retreat responses may be quite elaborate. For example, many shorebirds react to a disturbance by forming tight flocks that fly in an unpredictable course of retreat. The members of the flock maintain parallel positions and veer in unison. This defense response has been termed a *united erratic* or *social erratic*. Apparently, the motion of the flock produces a complex, changing stimulus that is not easy for predators to deal with.

COUNTERAGGRESSION

Under certain conditions, the stimulus that has been controlling retreat or immobility responses may produce counteraggressive behavior patterns. A classic example of counterattack upon the stimulus is the spring of the trapped rat. The mobbing behavior of birds is another instance of counteraggression. The repeated, rapid flights of the mobbing birds appear to effectively harass predators.

CLASSES OF FEAR STIMULI

As noted, the same stimulus characteristics that control exploration may also control fear. There are several additional types of stimuli that produce fear and withdrawal responses in many species. Four classes of these stimuli will be considered here.

LOOMING

When an object rapidly approaches an animal, the animal will frequently show some evasive response. We can simulate such a looming object in the laboratory by projecting a shadow that may be increased in size on a translucent screen in front of an animal (Schiff, 1965). Accelerated magnification of the shadow produces reactions like those seen in response to a real looming object. When subjects are presented with the reverse of the looming image—that is, with a shrinking shadow—these reactions are seen only rarely. Therefore, it is the looming aspect of the stimulus that is critical.

The evasive reactions seen to the looming shadow take different forms and occur in many taxa (Gibson, 1970; Hayes & Saiff, 1967; Schiff, 1965). Crabs run backward, flinch, or flatten out. Frogs jump away. Turtles pull their heads back into their shells. Chicks tense their bodies, run, hop, or crouch. Rhesus monkeys leap backward toward the rear of their cages. Humans tend to show a drop in skin resistance. Looming shadows of a wide variety of shapes are equally effective in eliciting these evasive responses.

DROP-OFFS

For obvious reasons, animals must avoid falling off the edges of high places. This avoidance of drop-offs can be studied in the laboratory with the use of an apparatus called a visual cliff (originally constructed by Gibson and Walk in 1960). As may be seen in Figure 6.3, in this type of apparatus the animal is placed on a center board over a sheet of glass.

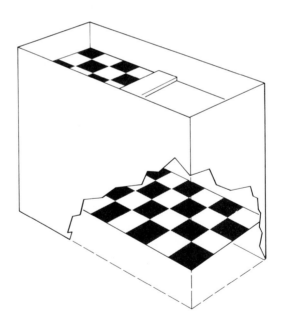

Figure 6.3

A visual cliff. The subject is placed on the central board, and its latency for stepping off onto the glass to either side is measured. The pattern is usually flush under the glass on one side and at some depth below it on the other.

A patterned surface is usually placed immediately under the glass on one side and at various depths below the glass on the other. This arrangement simulates a cliff with a drop-off to the deep side.

A variety of species avoid the deep side. Turtles, birds, various rodents, felines (including lions), sheep, goats, dogs, and primates go to the shallow side. Therefore, a wide range of vertebrates tend to avoid cliffs. Of course, some flying and swimming species are exempt from this type of fear response (see Gibson, 1970).

This drop-off avoidance develops quite early, and it appears in some taxa before any conventional type of learning could play a role in its genesis (see Gibson, 1970). Chicks and goats avoid the cliff when they are tested as soon as possible after birth, as do rats reared in the dark. Although 3- to 20-day-old monkeys do not locomote well, they show fear by freezing, crouching, vocalizing, self-clasping, and rocking back and forth when placed on the deep side of the visual cliff (Rosenblum & Cross, 1963). Human infants avoid the deep side as soon as they can crawl.

The stimulus controlling this fear reaction appears to be, in large part, the *motion parallax* produced by an animal near the edge of the drop-off. That is, when you move your eyes along the edge of a cliff, the ground on which you stand moves through your visual field much more rapidly than does the more distant ground beneath the cliff. The differential in speeds of movement between foreground and background constitutes motion parallax.

ALARM STIMULI

Many species have evolved alarm signals that are released by such stimuli as the appearance of a predator. The alarm signals produce fear responses in other members of the animal's species. For example, even before hatching, chicks become quiet and cease scratching motions in response to a maternal alarm call (Baeumer, 1955).

Sometimes members of one species react to the alarm stimuli produced by another. Tern alarm cries, for instance, release in harbor seals the alert posture that often precedes flight. In some cases, different species evolve very similar alarm signals. Consider the high, thin whistle that has been evolved by many songbirds in Europe and America. This whistle is like a pure tone that fades in and out, a tone that, in theory, makes the location of the source most difficult for a predator (see Marler & Hamilton, 1966).

WARNING COLORATION

The conspicuous coloration of many distasteful or poisonous animals may produce withdrawal reactions in predators. Such warning coloration tends to be relatively novel and intense; it often differs sharply from the animal's environmental background and appears bold and bright to the human eye. In several cases, it has been shown that this quality of novelty or intensity does not initially lead to withdrawal; instead, the predator must learn to avoid the warning stimuli. For example, the common and frequently unpalatable monarch butterfly possesses a bright and conspicuous pattern of orange and black in its wings (Brower, Ryerson, Coppinger, & Glazier, 1968). Vertebrate predators can rapidly learn to shun these and other aversive insects (Brower, 1958a, 1958b, 1958c; Brower & Brower, 1962).

Such a distinctively colored distasteful or dangerous animal may be mimicked by other species. Henry Bates, an English naturalist, was an early student of such mimicry. Bates observed that South American insectivorous birds, dragonflies, and lizards did not attack the numerous and conspicuous heliconiid butterflies; from this and other evidence, he deduced that they were distasteful to their predators. Also avoided by the predators were several other species of butterflies that showed a striking superficial resemblance to the heliconiids. In this resemblance to the heliconiids, these species were different in appearance from their near relatives. Bates reasoned that the mimics were harmless "counterfeits" of unpalatable heliconiid models and that their resemblance to these models afforded them protection against predators (Bates, 1862). Bates' reasoning has been accepted, and *Batesian mimicry* is the term used today to describe the imitation of an aversive species by an innocuous one.

Batesian mimicry can be quite elaborate in butterflies (Wickler, 1968). Some species are sexually dimorphic—male and female differ in appearance or size—with either the female or both the male and the female mimicking aversive models. Moreover, in some species with polymorphic female forms, some of the morphs (forms) may mimic different models. For example, the beautiful African *Papilio dardanus* has several female morphs, some of which mimic inedible models and some of which do not.

Sixteen years after Bates published his research, Müller described a second form of mimicry, in which several distasteful species resemble one another. In such *Müllerian mimicry,* each species benefits from the aversive qualities of the other. A predator can learn from one member of a Müllerian mimicry ring to avoid the other species that resemble it (Brower, Brower, & Collins, 1963).

Interestingly, in the recently described *Mertensian mimicry* (Wickler, 1968), quite deadly forms mimic less potent but aversive models. For example, the coral snake *Micrurus frontalis* possesses alternating bands of red, black, and yellow—hardly inconspicuous coloration. However, because its bite is lethal, no animal could learn to avoid this species; a predator's first experience would be its last. There are species of sublethal coral snakes, quite similarly marked, which can merely make predators ill. Apparently the lethal forms mimic the less poisonous models, which actually "teach" predators to avoid them.

The "eyespots" seen on caterpillars, butterflies (see Figure 6.4), fishes, and other animals are perhaps another instance of mimicry: these eyespots may mimic the appearance of a vertebrate's eyes. There is certainly evidence that such stimuli can release fear behaviors (Blest, 1957). In one experiment, inexperienced yellow buntings, European insectivorous birds, withdrew when displaying butterflies (*Nymphalis io*) opened their wings to reveal eyespots.

THE STIMULUS CONTROL OF EXPLORATION AND FEAR

Our examination of the areas of exploration and fear provides a good example of a common approach to the fundamental problem of the machinery or immediate causes of behavior. This approach takes the form of the analysis of the stimulus factors that control behavior. In the case of exploration and fear, we have seen that certain classes of stimulation can control the responses of many species of animals in a parallel fashion. For example, comparable withdrawal reactions to

Figure 6.4

Eyespots on the nymphalid Precis almana. From Blest, A. D., The function of eyespot patterns in the lepidoptera, *Behaviour*, 1957, *11*, p. 214. Reprinted by permission.

looming objects are found in many taxa. Furthermore, three types of stimulation produce either exploratory behavior or fear behavior, depending on their magnitude: complexity, novelty, and intensity are stimulus factors that, in different degrees, can yield either approach or withdrawal. This fact, along with the alternation that is often seen between the two types of behaviors, may be taken to suggest that there are similar mechanisms underlying some of the responses seen in exploration and fear.

BEHAVIOR IN TIME

From March to September, the grunion, a small atherinid fish, emerges from the sea to spawn on the beaches of southern California. Grunion do this at high tides during the nights that follow each new moon and full moon. Since on the southern California coast the highest tides occur at night during these phases of the moon, the eggs that are deposited during the receding high tides of the following few nights will remain undisturbed until the next series of high tides, about two weeks later. At this time, the eggs are usually washed from the sand, and the larvae hatch (Schwassmann, 1971; Walker, 1949, 1952).

As do the events of the grunion's semilunar spawning cycle, many behaviors fall into rhythmic patterns. These patterns vary tremendously in their *period,* or the time it takes for a single cycle to occur. The period of a cycle may have a duration of years, months, days, hours, minutes, seconds, or milliseconds. For example, pairs of the nearly extinct California condor can produce only a single offspring every two years (Koford, 1953; McMillan, 1968). Your heart, on the other hand, normally beats slightly more than once a second when you are at rest, and the heart of a song sparrow beats about once every 130 milliseconds (Odum, 1945).

Any point or portion of a behavioral cycle may be called a *phase.* The California condor may be in the incubation phase of its biennial reproductive rhythm. Your heart may be at the phase in its cycle when the left ventricle contracts. Sometimes the behavioral rhythm may be *in phase* with natural cycles in the world outside the organism. Events in the condor's reproductive process occur in their season: for example, courtship takes place in winter, hatching in spring. In contrast, the phases of your heartbeat are normally not synchronous with external stimuli.

There are two ways in which behavioral cycles can originate. A cycle may be a direct response to some rhythmic external stimulus, or it may be timed by some kind of "clock" within the organism. In the case in which a behavioral cycle is entirely governed by rhythmic events in the world outside the organism, it can be said that the cycle is under *exogenous* control. For example, the fact that European tits, small insectivorous birds, prey on certain species of caterpillars in the summer reflects the annual cycle of availability of the prey (L. Tinbergen, 1960).

In the case in which a behavioral rhythm can occur independently of cyclic external stimuli, it is said that the pattern is under *endogenous* control. In order to demonstrate that a pattern is endogenous, one must have experimental evidence of two types. First, one must show that the rhythm persists in an environment that one has attempted to keep constant in all critical aspects. Second, since there is always a possibility that one has unintentionally left some subtle but important stimulus free to vary, the rhythm must be observed to drift *out of phase* with the external cycles that usually accompany it outside the laboratory. For example, consider the activity rhythm of the shanny, a small blennid fish that lives in the intertidal zone on many European shores. In England, the shanny may be found in tidepools when the tide is out and can usually feed on barnacles, its primary prey, only when the tide is higher. In the laboratory, a shanny placed under constant conditions shows an approximately twice-a-day activity rhythm that persists for several cycles (Gibson, 1967). Initially, the fish is active when high tide would be occurring in its natural environment, but later its rhythm drifts out of phase with the local tides. The persistence of the rhythm, although it is limited, and the drift of the rhythm may be taken to indicate that the tidal cycle is endogenous in the shanny.

Note that such endogenous activity rhythms are not free from external influences under natural conditions: they are almost invariably in phase with some major environmental cycle. An endogenous rhythm tied to such an external cycle is said to be *entrained*. *Entrainment* is accomplished when some stimulus in the environment brings the endogenous rhythm under *phase control*. In the case of the shanny, sudden drops in water temperature, such as naturally occur when a tidepool is flooded by a rising tide, are stimuli that can bring the fish's activity into phase in the laboratory. The critical stimulus in such an entrainment is called a *Zeitgeber*, which means "time-giver" in German.

CIRCADIAN RHYTHMS

Most vertebrates show a daily behavioral rhythm. These cycles are typically composed of a time of activity (sometimes symbolized by the Greek letter α) and a time of rest (symbolized by the Greek letter ρ). (See Aschoff, Klotter, & Wever, 1965, for a discussion of these and other terms.) In different species, activity time and rest time have a characteristic relationship to the daily light-dark cycle, often abbreviated LD. Some species are *diurnal,* or day-active; some are *nocturnal;* and some are *crepuscular*—active in twilight.

In most studies, these daily rhythms persist under constant experimental conditions. Let's compare the flying squirrel's nocturnal activity

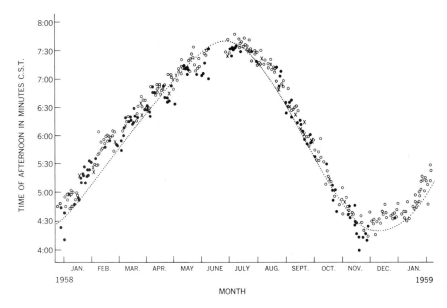

Figure 7.1

Circles indicate the time at the beginning of running-wheel activity in a flying squirrel under natural lighting. ● represents skies more than 8% cloudy, X skies from 7% to 8% cloudy, and O skies less than 7% cloudy. From DeCoursey, P. J. Phase control and activity in a rodent, *Cold Spring Harbor Symposia in Quantitative Biology*, 1960, *25*, 50–51. © 1960 by Cold Spring Harbor Laboratory. Reprinted by permission.

pattern under normal LD with its activity pattern under constant darkness. As you can see in Figure 7.1, the onset of the squirrel's activity is at dusk under normal conditions. When the squirrel is kept in constant darkness, its activity pattern drifts out of phase with the local LD, as you can see in Figure 7.2. Incidentally, note that this free-running cycle (the endogenous rhythm of the squirrel) is marked by great precision: the onset of each activity time is predictable within a few minutes. Since the period of this cycle, like that of other flying squirrels kept in darkness, is less than 24 hours, the rhythm is not daily in a strict sense. The term *circadian,* from the Latin *circa diem,* meaning "about a day," has been coined to describe rhythms with a period of about 24 hours. The facts that the cycle is free-running in conditions of constant darkness and that it drifts out of phase with the LD, of course, constitute the evidence for endogenous control in this behavioral cycle.

Circadian rhythms under constant conditions are seen in many aspects of behavior and in various bodily functions. One particularly

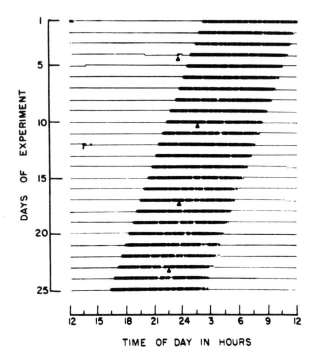

Figure 7.2

Running-wheel activity of a flying squirrel kept in total darkness. Rotation of the activity wheel is shown by the thicker lines. Triangles indicate times of feeding. From DeCoursey, P. J. Phase control and activity in a rodent, *Cold Spring Harbor Symposia in Quantitative Biology,* 1960, *25*, 50–51. © 1960 by Cold Spring Harbor Laboratory. Reprinted by permission.

well-studied species is our own. In this research, people are kept under relatively constant environmental conditions—often in a bunker or a cave—without knowing the time. Under such conditions, persisting circadian rhythms are seen in circulation, temperature, metabolic rate, sleepiness, and other bodily functions (see Conroy & Mills, 1970; Mills, 1966). Many of these rhythms drift out of phase with local LD and therefore may be considered endogenous.

There are individual variations in the timing of the behavioral events that take place within circadian cycles. For instance, in a particular human under normal LD, the peak of performance in a battery of tests and the peak in body temperature may typically occur in the morning, afternoon, or evening of his active period. In other words, there may be "morning people," "afternoon people," and "evening people" (see Kleitman, 1963), just as is commonly believed.

Aschoff's rule. The period of a free-running circadian rhythm is not always the same: different constant conditions can produce different periodicities. Light level, for example, typically affects vertebrate circadian rhythms in two ways, as Aschoff pointed out in 1960. First, for nocturnal species, the period of a circadian rhythm is ordinarily longer the more brightly lit the experimental chamber. For instance, as you can see in Figure 7.3, the house mouse's average subjective day was about 23 hours long in a light level comparable to moonlight and was nearly 26 hours long in light like that of an ordinary laboratory room. Second, for diurnal species, the opposite is usually true: for example, the chaffinch in Figure 7.3 showed about a 25-hour day in dim illumination and a 22-hour day under the brightest lighting tested. This statement of the relationship among favored time of activity, level of illumination, and period has come to be called Aschoff's rule.

Entrainment. In most vertebrates, a change in light level acts as the Zeitgeber in the entrainment of circadian rhythms. As you see in Figure 7.4, imposing a certain LD schedule (6.5 hours of light to 17.5 hours of darkness) on the nocturnal hamster, previously kept in constant darkness, causes its activity to gradually come into phase with the new experimental day (DeCoursey, 1964). Note that the animal "resets" the time of onset of its active period in a series of steps until it attains a proper phase relationship to the LD—that is, until its activity

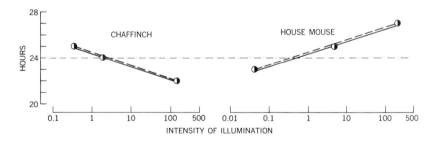

Figure 7.3

The relationship of circadian period to constant light level. According to Aschoff's rule, the free-running period of a nocturnal animal such as a house mouse increases with level of illumination. In a diurnal animal, such as the chaffinch, the free-running period decreases as light level increases. From Aschoff, J., Exogenous and endogenous components in circadian rhythms, *Cold Spring Harbor Symposia in Quantitative Biology,* 1960, *25,* 16. © 1960 by Cold Spring Harbor Laboratory. Reprinted by permission.

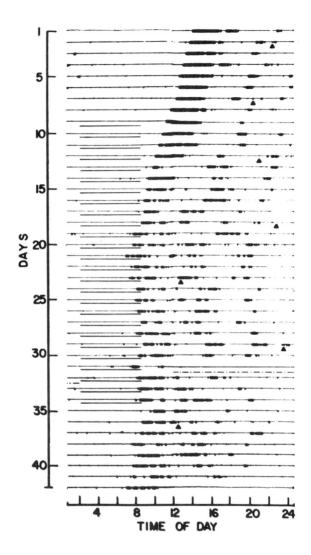

Figure 7.4

Entrainment of a free-running hamster on a light schedule of 6.5 hours of light to 17.5 hours of darkness. The bar beneath the wheel-activity record indicates that the light is on. From DeCoursey, P. J. Function of a light response rhythm in hamsters, *Journal of Cellular and Comparative Physiology,* 1964, *63,* 189–196. Reprinted by permission.

occurs in the dark. In all vertebrates studied, the size of such steps varies with the phase of the animal's active time at which the light change occurs. For example, consider the effect of a 10-minute light period, or "light shock," imposed on a flying squirrel kept in constant darkness (DeCoursey, 1961). As you see in Figure 7.5, for most of the flying squirrel's inactive time, the light has no effect. However, if the light shock is presented at the time when the squirrel normally becomes active, there is a delay in the onset of the squirrel's next activity period. If the light shock is presented later in the squirrel's activity period, the delaying effect of the light shock will be of less magnitude. After a certain point in the squirrel's activity period, there is a reversal: presenting the light shock will cause an advance in the onset of the next activity period. Finally, the advancing effect diminishes as the flying squirrel's subjective night ends.

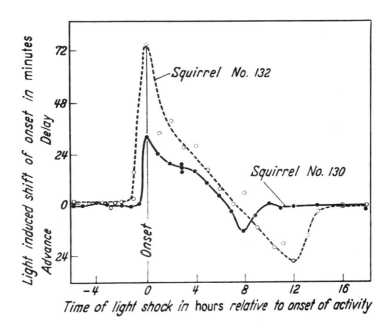

Figure 7.5

Response to 10-minute light shocks in two flying squirrels. From DeCoursey, P. J. Effect of light on the circadian activity rhythm of the flying squirrel, *Glaucomys volans, Zeitschrift für vergleichende Physiologie,* 1961, *44,* 331–354. Reprinted by permission.

YEARLY RHYTHMS

Behavior follows an annual cycle in most temperate-zone species. During this yearly cycle, species-characteristic events such as migration, hibernation, establishment of territories, formation of colonies, pair bonding, and defending young all find their place. What controls the timing of these events? Do endogenous annual "clocks" play a role? To what extent is control of this type of behavior exogenous?

Data on these questions are incomplete. However, it is clear that both external and endogenous factors can be important. Perhaps the best-studied annual phenomena are the reproductive cycles of migratory birds. It has been known for centuries that *photoperiod*, the daily duration of light, can affect these cycles. The Japanese, for example, long ago practiced the art of *Yogai*, in which they made birds sing in winter by exposing them to candlelight for three or four hours after nightfall (Welty, 1962). The first scientific reaffirmation of such effects was made by William Rowan (see Orr, 1970; Rowan, 1929, 1938). Rowan, working in Alberta in the 1920s, showed that artificial increases in the length of photoperiod in winter produced increases in the size of the gonads of the slate-colored junco. When Rowan released the juncos in midwinter, many of his experimental birds soon left the area, whereas controls exposed to the normal winter light did not. When similar experimentation was conducted with crows, their gonad weight also increased. When released, some of the experimental animals moved out of the area in the northwestern direction (the direction habitually taken for their spring migration), whereas controls remained in the area or went southwest. The results of these experiments with juncos and crows suggest that both gonad growth and migratory behavior can be entrained by photoperiod.

Since Rowan's pioneering research, many other studies with songbirds have produced a similar result: lengthening photoperiod induces gonad growth. Along with this effect, there are increases in general activity and metabolic levels. In migratory species, fat deposition and *Zugunruhe*, or migratory restlessness, may be seen (Orr, 1970).

Interestingly, in at least some species of birds, vision is not necessary in order for photoperiod to have its effects (Menaker, 1971, 1972). Experiments with house sparrows have shown that the avian brain itself can be directly sensitive to light, and it is apparently by this means that photoperiod influences the sparrow's annual cycle of behavior. Direct light transmission to the brain is also involved in photoperiodic effects in ducks. You can demonstrate that such light transmission through skin and bone is in fact quite possible by repeating the childhood experiment of looking at the light transmitted through your hand by a flashlight held against your fingers or palm (Menaker, 1972).

Although photoperiod may help to control annual cycles in many species of birds, endogenous factors may also play a role. One endogenous limitation on photoperiodic control is the refractory period that follows normal summer breeding. During this period, many species of animals cannot be brought into reproductive condition by imposing increased photoperiods. For example, after their February-to-June breeding season, male starlings exposed to constant light would first begin to show changes in their reproductive state only in September (Schwab, 1971).

Another endogenous factor in some species is the yearly rhythm itself. When members of such species are kept under constant conditions, the yearly cycle repeats itself like a circadian rhythm. For example, under a constant day with 12 hours of light and 12 hours of darkness the willow warbler goes through its usual cycle of moult and migratory restlessness (Gwinner, 1971). However, since the period of the cycle may deviate somewhat from a year, the term "annual" is inexact. Recently, on the model of the term circadian, the word *circannual* was devised to describe rhythms with a period of about a year.

In species of birds with such circannual rhythms, photoperiod may be the Zeitgeber in the more precise timing of events. For example, in the slate-colored junco, photoperiod can advance or delay endogenous annual events such as migratory fat deposition and testes growth (Wolfson, 1960).

Phenomena similar to those seen in birds have been described for other vertebrate taxa. For example, photoperiodic influences on annual reproductive rhythms have been observed in fishes, amphibians, reptiles, and mammals (Farner, 1965; Rowan, 1938). Free-running circannual rhythms have been demonstrated in striped plateau lizards (Stebbins, 1963) and in some mammals (Goss, 1969).

The most thoroughly investigated case of endogenous annual rhythms in mammals is that of the golden-mantled ground squirrel of the Rocky Mountains. Pengelley and Fisher (1957, 1961, 1963; Pengelley & Asmundson, 1969, 1971) first noted this rhythm while studying the squirrel's hibernation. In August, they put a squirrel in a small room without windows. This room was illuminated on a schedule of 12 hours of light to 12 hours of darkness, and its temperature was held at 0°C (32°F). Initially the squirrel remained active, eating and drinking, and its body temperature remained normal at 37°C (98.6°F). In October, the squirrel ceased these activities and hibernated, its body temperature falling to 1°C (33.8°F). In April, the squirrel became active again, with normal body temperature. In September, it resumed hibernation. This alternating pattern of activity and hibernation was exhibited by other golden-mantled ground squirrels under constant conditions. Its typical period lasted about 300 days and therefore was clearly circannual. Because of its persistence and drift under constant conditions, this cycle could be regarded as endogenous. Interestingly, photoperiod does not appear to be the key Zeitgeber for this rhythm; rather, it seems that temperature may play a major role in its entrainment. This is a sensible arrangement, considering that the squirrel, which spends a great deal of time in its burrow, may not be affected by changes in the length of the day.

REPRODUCTIVE CYCLES

Many species are not limited to a single reproductive sequence per year; instead, such species may reproduce several times within a breeding season or, in some cases, may go through successive reproductive cycles throughout the year. Great progress has been made in the investigation of the physiological and behavioral mechanisms underlying such cycles. As an illustration of this progress, let's consider the case of the ring dove, so intensively studied by Lehrman and his colleagues (Lehrman, 1961, 1964a, 1964b; Lott, 1973).

In the laboratory, the following sequence of behavior is reliably seen in each of the ring dove's reproductive cycles. At the beginning of a cycle, the male dove bows, coos, and struts about the cage. After a few hours of this, the male and then the female crouch in the nesting bowl and give a distinctive nest call. Then, for a week, both birds participate in building the nest. Typically, the male collects materials and brings them to his mate, who does the actual construction. During this week, the birds copulate. Seven to eleven days after copulation began, the female lays her first egg—typically at around five o'clock in the afternoon—and begins to incubate. Two days later, she lays a second —typically at around nine o'clock in the morning. On that day and thereafter, the male and female take daily turns sitting on the eggs. After about fourteen days, the young hatch, and the parents begin to feed the squabs crop milk (cells sloughed off by the parent birds' crop lining). The mates continue to feed the squabs after they leave the nest and as they become independent. Finally, after two or three weeks of parental care, the squabs are ignored. At this point, courtship begins anew and the cycle is repeated.

From their extensive research on the ring dove, Lehrman and his associates have concluded that the reproductive sequence involves several behavior-hormone interactions. Briefly, the presence of a courting male and of nesting material induces the production of the hormone estrogen in the female. Estrogen leads to nest-building, which causes the release of the hormone progesterone. Both progesterone and estrogen lead to ovulation. Progesterone appears to produce incubation behavior and may facilitate parental feeding responses. Participation in incubation and the stimulation provided by the young result, in both sexes, in the secretion of the hormone prolactin, which leads to the enlargement of the crop gland and facilitates parental feeding behavior.

Research such as Lehrman's has helped us to understand the physiological bases of cyclic behavior. Further investigation should reveal more about the precise neural pathways that mediate behavioral rhythms.

THE ORGANISMIC BASES FOR BEHAVIOR CYCLES

This chapter illustrates a second basic approach to the problem of the machinery of behavior: the analysis of the organism's reaction to stimuli. Research on behavioral rhythms indicates that the influence of external stimuli is not always direct; in the case of many behavioral cycles, it has been demonstrated that the organism possesses a kind of clockwork mechanism through which an environmental stimulus produces its effect. The external stimulus acts to "set" this clockwork and thus indirectly controls the timing of events. Moreover, research has specified some of the hormonal changes that serve as part of the physiological machinery determining behavioral rhythms. The study of these cycles has taught us much about the role of the organism as a determinant of behavior.

In eastern Canada, the choruses of the spring peeper, a tree frog, begin to resound as the last snow and ice melt. In this species, the males provide the voices for the choruses, and their peeps attract both males and females to breeding sites (see Goin & Goin, 1971). Both the calls and the other frogs' approaches to the choruses are part of the *social behavior* of the spring peeper. Social behavior comprises those responses that an animal makes to members of its own species. Social behavior varies greatly in extent and complexity among the vertebrates. At one end of the spectrum, members of a species may be solitary and may actively avoid each other. They may approach each other only when they mate and care for young. At the opposite end, members of a species may be integrated into large groups characterized by elaborate social structures. In such groups, the behavior of individuals will often be highly coordinated. In this chapter, we will consider this range of vertebrate social behavior. We will start by considering those responses that tend to increase or decrease the distance between members of the same species. Next, we will survey the types of social structures that exist for those species that come together to form animal societies. Then we will examine the synchronization of behaviors in social groups. Finally, we will entertain the question of the adaptive significance of many of the social behaviors described.

Before we begin this introduction to social behavior, let's cover a few definitions. Members of the same species are called *conspecifics*. This word is derived from Latin roots meaning "together with" and "particular kind" or "species." The adjective *intraspecific* is used to describe the interactions of conspecifics. As you might guess, this term comes from the Latin equivalents for "within species." The contrasting term *interspecific*, from the Latin for "between species," is employed to describe interactions of members of different species. To give an example of the use of these terms, one red-eared turtle is the conspecific of another; the male's curious courtship of the female, in which he swims before her and vibrates his toenails against her face and the side of her head (see Carr, 1952), is an intraspecific interaction. In contrast, the capture of crayfish by the red-eared turtle is an interspecific event. It should be noted that social behavior can sometimes occur interspecifically. For instance, typical intraspecific behavior may often occur among *congeners*, members of the same genus. Such interactions are often seen when closely related species form mixed social groups in which their responses to their conspecifics and their congeners are identical.

DISPERSION AND SOCIAL BEHAVIOR

In the language of ecology, *dispersion* refers to the distribution of animals in space at any moment in time. This distribution is almost invariably the immediate consequence of behavior: animals may approach or avoid some physical feature in their environment, or they may be attracted or repelled by their conspecifics. Because of this attraction or repulsion for conspecifics, the dispersion of most species is intimately related to their social behavior. This section will describe some of the basic fashions in which animals arrange themselves in space.

HOME RANGE

Vertebrates do not always wander at liberty through their habitat; instead, they often become tied to some small portion of their environment. The area to which an animal restricts its activities is often called its *home range*. Restriction of movement to a home range can occur for social or nonsocial reasons. As an example of the latter, consider the red deer in northwestern Scotland that were so intensively studied by Darling (1937). Hinds (mature females) and young red deer formed stable groups that were rarely observed to stray from well-defined home ranges. Indeed, in an experiment designed to test a hind group's faithfulness to its range, Darling failed in repeated attempts to lure a group across its boundaries with food that would ordinarily be accepted. He observed no obvious avoidance or retreat responses to other red deer, which would limit any hind group's movements to its home range; it seemed that only fear of novel ground restricted the group's movement. This hypothesis was suggested by the only invasion of a new area he witnessed, during which the colonizing hind group showed pronounced fear responses.

A similar case is that of the coati, a relative of the raccoon. On Barro Colorado Island, Panama, Kaufmann (1962) observed that bands of coati occupied overlapping home ranges. Each band spent most of its time in a portion of the home range called the *core area* and visited the rest at irregular intervals (see Figure 8.1). While the coati were either in the core area or in other parts of the home range, the bands "fed and moved with no signs of uneasiness or unfamiliarity" (p. 167). However, in the coatis' rare movements outside the range, Kaufmann observed fearful behaviors, such as a constant running back and forth.

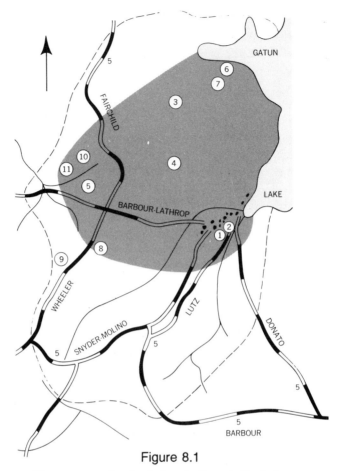

Figure 8.1

Home range of a single band of coati. Circled num-
bers show roost trees. Shaded portion indicates the
core area. Broken lines define the limits of the home
range. From Kaufmann, J. H. *Ecology and Social
Behavior of the Coati, Nasua Narica, on Barro Colorado Island, Panama,* University of California Press
Publications in Zoology, 1962, *60*(3). Originally published by the University of California Press. Reprinted by permission of the Regents of the
University of California.

Within its home range, the animal's movement can also be restricted by nonsocial factors. For example, in the red deer, the sudden
onset of cold would drive herds of hinds and their young from the high,
exposed part of their home range. Nonsocial stimuli may lead to approach behavior as well. For instance, the coati observed by Kaufmann

traveled out of their core area to feed on fruit that was seasonally available in other parts of their home range.

In other species, social factors may act to limit movements to or within a home range. For example, in a study of the mountain lion in the Rocky Mountains (Hornocker, 1969), resident males were observed to occupy home ranges that contained no other male lions except for an occasional transient. Females occupied smaller home ranges that overlapped with those of males and those of other females. In general, both resident males and females avoided each other and any transients; close contact was observed only during the breeding season and while a female had dependent young. One factor important in maintaining avoidance was the scrape marks found on trails, ridges, and "lion crossings." At these points, passing lions urinated and often defecated. When lions being tracked were observed to have veered or retraced their paths at a scrape mark, another lion or a lioness with cubs proved to be in the vicinity. Presumably, recently deposited urine or feces mediated the avoidance of contact.

The mountain lion therefore appears to be "antisocial"; yet, since its antisocial responses are made to its conspecifics, they represent one form of social behavior. Another form of social behavior prominent in the control of movements within the home range is territorial defense.

TERRITORY

In many animal species, part or all of a home range may be defended. That is, a resident may attack or make aggressive displays toward intruders along the borders of his home range or in certain areas of it. The space defended is commonly called a *territory*.[1] Territorial defense is most frequently intraspecific, but interspecific territorial conflicts may be seen in some species. Territorial behavior is often seasonal, and different forms of social behavior may replace it at other times. Several types of territories are often distinguished, but it should be recognized that these types are regarded as points on a continuum rather than as exclusive categories. The following classification follows those of Nice (1941) and Welty (1962).

Feeding, rearing, and mating territories. Some species defend their entire home range against conspecifics. All their activities of feeding, mating, and rearing occur within territorial limits. Drawn on maps, these territories resemble little independent states with boundaries and capitals. Consider the territories of the palm warblers shown in Figure 8.2 (Welsh, 1971). These small insectivorous birds arrived at this Nova

---

[1] It should be noted that other definitions of territory exist. For example, a few writers equate territory with home range. Here we will follow the common usage of territory to mean a defended area.

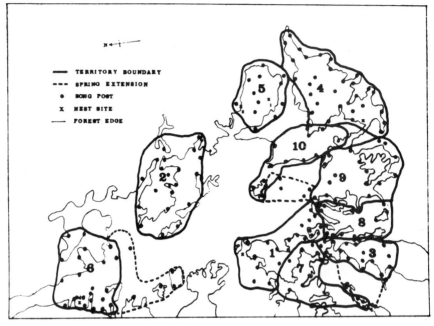

Figure 8.2

Territories of the palm warbler. From Welsh, D. A. Breeding and territoriality of the palm warbler in a Nova Scotian bog. *Canadian Field Naturalist,* 1971, *85,* 31–37. Reprinted with permission from *Canadian Field Naturalist.*

Scotian bog in May. The males immediately began to establish territories ranging in size between two and one-half and five acres. Natural delineations, such as forest edges, often served as borders. During this period, the new male residents showed aggression by chasing singing intruders. The borders of the territories, once established, remained rather stable, and aggression largely ceased. However, the territory owners continued to sing throughout the season, frequently from favorite song posts on tamarack trees. All their activities of courtship, nesting, and rearing took place within their territorial limits.

A mammalian example of a similar type of territorial behavior is that of the female red and Douglas squirrels studied in the Cascade Mountains of British Columbia by Smith (1968). Single squirrels of both sexes were observed to maintain nonoverlapping territories throughout the year. Defense took the forms of vocalizations and chasing. Only in breeding season was this territorial pattern of dispersion altered: males were tolerated in females' territories during the time the owner was in heat. Interestingly, red and Douglas squirrels defended territories from each other; intruders reacted similarly to interspecific and intraspecific territorial calls.

Mating and rearing territories. In some species, the area defended includes mating and rearing sites, but much or all of the defender's feeding is done outside its territorial boundaries. For instance, the polygynous male redwing blackbird defends a territory that often includes more than one female nest. Pairing and nesting occur here, but feeding is not restricted to the territory. These territories are well defined and are often easy to observe, since the redwing is not timid and frequently defends areas that include open marsh (Nero, 1956; Orians, 1961).

A similar form of territoriality in fish is shown by the male darter *Etheostoma exile* (Winn, 1958). This darter defends a small territory along the shore of a lake and feeds both inside and outside this area (see Figure 8.3). Pairs of darters spawn within the territory. Since the male continues to defend the territory after spawning, the eggs are thus protected against conspecifics.

Mating territories. Territories that consist of a mating site alone are frequently found in close proximity and are always defended or advertised by rather conspicuous means. A group of adjoining mating

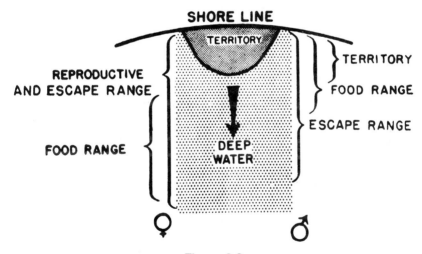

Figure 8.3

Territory of the male darter Etheostoma exile. From Winn, H. E. Comparative reproductive behaviour and ecology of fourteen species of darters (Pisces-Pericidae), *Ecological Monographs,* 1958, *28,* 167. Copyright 1958 The Ecological Society of America. Reprinted by permission.

territories is called an *arena*. In birds, the arena is often called a *lek*. The individual territories comprising an arena are called *courts*. Consider Armstrong's (1947) description of the mating territory of the ruff, a European shorebird.

A number of circular courts a foot or two in diameter mark the scene of the bird's trysts and tourneys. A wayfarer unacquainted with the strange customs of the ruff would be greatly puzzled to account for these bare patches arranged in a pattern in the midst of flower-studded meadows. Year after year the ruff return to the same plot and attitudinise like feathered marionettes; and to these known places of assignation come the reeves [female ruffs] to choose their mates. So faithful are the birds to their "hill" that when a road was made over one of them they did not desert it [p. 217].

The California sea lion (Peterson & Bartholomew, 1967) is an example of a mammalian taxon in which only a mating territory is defended. Breeding sites for this subspecies range northward from the Mexican coast at Mazatlán to the California Channel Islands. On the Channel Islands, bulls maintain a string of territories along various shores during May, June, July, and August. Bulls on territories bark incessantly and periodically engage in the "boundary ceremony" with their neighbors.

[The bulls] rush toward each other, barking rapidly, with vibrissae extended anteriorly. Just before reaching the boundary between their territories they stop barking and fall on their chests, open their mouths widely, shake their heads rapidly from side to side, and weave their necks laterally at a rate much slower than the head-shaking which is simultaneously going on. They then rear themselves to a maximum height, twist their heads sideways, and stare obliquely at each other. . . . This process is ritualized, and the animals do not touch each other; if they happen to be unusually close together they skillfully avoid contact. Sometimes during the boundary ceremony the two bulls partially cross the boundary and stand side by side, facing opposite directions, making feinting jabs at the chest and flippers of each other. The oblique stare is often the last component of the display prior to the bulls' separation, or prior to repetition of the entire head shaking, neck weaving sequence.*

An unritualized version of the boundary ceremony occurs when an intruder challenges the territory holder. The challenge comes in the form of the intruder's direct and silent approach to the resident bull. A violent conflict ensues, in which bouts of head-weaving, lunges, bites, and falls on the chest are separated by short intervals during which the bulls rear up face to face "as if to tower" over one another. Should the challenger win, he typically replaces the territory holder and begins to bark and perform the boundary ceremony with his neighbors. Because

*From Peterson, R. S., and Bartholomew, G. A. *The Natural History and Behavior of the California Sea Lion,* 1967. Reprinted by permission of the American Society of Mammalogists.

of these fierce fights, only a few bulls can retain a territory for more than two weeks (Peterson & Bartholomew, 1967).

Some species of birds that hold mating territories do more than merely defend a court; the court itself may be specially constructed. For example, the magnificent bird of paradise of New Guinea clears a wide area around a sapling and crops the overhanging leaves so that sunlight can play on its iridescent plumage as it displays in its court (Gilliard, 1958; Rand, 1940).

Some of the most spectacular arena species are the bowerbirds of New Guinea and Australia. These birds go further than simply clearing an area; they build various structures to attract females (see Gilliard, 1963, 1969; Marshall, 1954). Whereas the courts built by some species are quite simple, those of others can be very elaborate (see Gilliard, 1963). For instance, Archbold's bowerbird makes a simple "table-sized" stage on the ground, which it "carpets . . . with ferns, and decorates . . . with shafts of bamboo, poles of resin, beetle skeletons, snail shells and lumps of charcoal." More elaborate is the construction of the satin bowerbird (Chaffer, 1961; Marshall, 1954). The male erects an avenue by thrusting two parallel rows of twigs into a base of twigs or grass (Figure 8.4). Many males paint the inner walls of their corridors black. To do this, the bird may use a bit of chewed bark as a "kind of combination sponge, wedge and stopper" that holds its beak open and facilitates painting. Saliva and charcoal serve as paint. The bird also decorates his court; he prefers blue or greenish-yellow "trinkets" and flowers, although pure yellow, brown, and gray items are acceptable. The female satin bowerbird is attracted to the male's court and mates with him there. It should be noted that many of the bowerbirds have what is called an *extended arena*; that is, their courts are located in the same general vicinity but are not contiguous.

Small rearing territories. In many species, defense is limited to a small area around the rearing site. Such species are often colonial: their territories are found in aggregations, often at traditional sites. For instance, on certain islands and in flat, open areas, herring gulls form colonies during each breeding season. In these colonies, each male herring gull defends a territory around his nest by displaying and fighting. Within this territory, the gulls lay and brood their eggs and care for their young (Tinbergen, 1953).

Feeding territories. Feeding areas are defended in some species. One form of such territoriality in fish may be seen in many immature trout and salmon. For example, juvenile Atlantic salmon were observed to hold territories in rapids on the Miramichi River of New Brunswick (Keenleyside & Yamamoto, 1962). From a "station" within these territories, the young salmon sallied out to attack intruders or to feed.

Figure 8.4

Male satin bowerbird constructing its bower. From Chaffer, N. Bower building and display in the satin bowerbird, *Australian Zoologist,* 1959, *12,* 295–305. Reprinted by permission of the Gould League of New South Wales.

In birds, feeding territories are held by certain species in winter. For example, red-headed woodpeckers were observed to establish small territories in a Maryland wood during the fall (Kilham, 1958). Within their territories, these conspicuous woodpeckers hid acorns, which they consumed throughout the winter. Defense of their territories was both interspecific and intraspecific: the red-headed woodpeckers chased away titmice, blue jays, and woodpeckers of most other species, as well as their conspecifics.

In other species of birds, some individuals may continue to defend their summer territories in winter. For instance, some European robins were seen to defend in December all or part of the territories they had held in April (Lack, 1943).

Group territories. The territories described so far have been those occupied either by a single animal or by mates engaged in reproductive activities. Territories can also be defended by groups of animals. One example of group territoriality is that of the Galapagos mockingbird *Nesomimus macdonaldi.* Near the coast of Hood Island, small "bands" of mockingbirds were observed defending a common territory by Hatch (1966). Infrequent lone intruders into the territory were driven out by one or more members of the resident band. When two bands met near a territory boundary, a dancing display ensued. Members of each band arrayed themselves on "either side of an imaginary line" and took jerky steps forward, backward, and sideways. These steps were accompanied by wing flashes, tail flips, and "head-up" or "head-forward" postures.

An interesting form of group-territorial behavior was described in a study of the black-tailed prairie dog in the Black Hills of South Dakota (King, 1955). These prairie dogs lived only in their "towns" and were not found in otherwise suitable habitat in the surrounding area. Each prairie dog town was subdivided into territories, which were defended by small social groups called *coteries*. Coterie members kissed and groomed each other, engaged in mutual play, and shared access to all the burrows within their common territory. Intruders into their territory were greeted with barking, "rushing," chasing, and biting.

TAXONOMY AND TERRITORIALITY

Territoriality occurs in some groups of animals and not in others. (See the review by Brown & Orians, 1970.) Territoriality is seen in many bony fishes, which frequently defend their courting sites. Among amphibians, territorial behavior has been reported in frogs (see Wiewandt, 1969) and salamanders. Defended areas are small, and they appear to center on courting, resting, or nesting sites. Among reptiles, diurnal lizards often show territoriality. (Territoriality in iguanid lizards is reviewed in Carpenter, 1967.) No intraspecific territoriality has yet been observed in snakes, turtles, or crocodilians. Birds have been particularly well studied, and only a few species exist that do not show territorial behavior of some form. Although defense of different types of territory is seen in some mammalian species, others show no territorial behavior. Nevertheless, in quite a few of these latter cases, the home range of a species member may not overlap with that of a conspecific of the same sex and age range. For example, in several mammalian carnivores, males possess such exclusive home ranges, yet they do not actively display at or attack other males. In these instances, it seems that their scent marks have the same effect as active territorial defense and that their home range is functionally equivalent to a territory. Several writers (for example, Brown & Orians, 1970) have suggested that such scent marking be considered territorial behavior and that such an exclusive home range be considered a territory.

FREE SPACE

Animals often keep more than their territory clear of conspecifics; the space near the animal, its mate, or its offspring may also be kept free of intruders. This maintenance of a free space may occur within the bounds of the animal's territory or home range, or it may occur in undefended and unfamiliar areas—for example, during wintering or migration. There are two ways in which free space can be maintained: through retreat when the intruder comes too close or through proximity defense—that is, the challenge of intruders by attack or display. Here I will distinguish only two simple forms of free space, *individual distance* and *mate distance*.

Individual distance. Individuals of many species maintain a certain distance around themselves free of conspecifics. Such distance may be easily observed in a row of gulls along a roof ridge (see Figure 8.5) or in a flock of swallows on a telephone line: a characteristic minimum interval exists between individuals within which approach is not tolerated. The way in which such individual distance contributes to the regularity of spacing in such aggregations was first investigated in the laboratory by Crook (1961). In aviaries with a single long perch, Crook observed flocks of the weaver finches *Quelea quelea quelea, Euplectes afra,* and *Sitagra melanocephala.* These species maintained a typical *arrival distance:* individuals of a species would join a flock on the perch at a certain average distance from the next animal. Following an arrival, the birds often readjusted their positions to establish a *settled distance.* In the process of readjustment, the newcomer frequently came closer

Figure 8.5
Individual distance. Photograph by the author.

to other animals after it landed at one end of the flock, well outside the individual distance of its nearest neighbor. If, instead, the newcomer landed between two birds on the perch, the two often shifted away from the new arrival as their individual distance was transgressed, following which a shunting process ensued, in which all other birds in the line shuffled in turn as their individual distances were violated. In other cases, however, aggression might be the consequence of an approach within individual distance.

Individual distance, of course, varies with species. For instance, black-headed gulls on London rooftops were seen to react to other individuals that came within a body length by retreating or threatening, whereas tufted ducks in St. James Park allowed approach only to within two or three body lengths (Condor, 1949).

Individual distance may vary also with sex. Marler (1956b) has provided us with an experimental study of sex differences in individual distance in the chaffinch. The measurement of these differences was made using two movable food hoppers in a large cage. Marler determined the average distance between the hoppers at which one bird would drive away another. In two flocks of eight males, the mean distances at which this occurred were 21 cm and 24 cm; in two flocks of eight females, retreat occurred at 7 cm in each case. Males were more tolerant toward females than toward males in two mixed flocks of four males and four females; the male-female distance averaged 12 cm and 8 cm.

It should be noted that not all species maintain individual distance. In fact, many species routinely come into contact for long periods as they engage in such activities as resting or mutual grooming. Examples of *contact* species are wild boars, porcupines, tortoises, and many monkeys (Hediger, 1955).

In contrast, in some species, individual distances are maintained not only among conspecifics but also among members of closely related taxa. For instance, in mixed-species flocks of swallows, individuals of one species will maintain a space free from members of both their own and other species. Differing from this interspecific individual distance is the space animals keep free of possible predators. In many species, animals will flee a potential predator if it comes too close. This *flight distance* is species-characteristic. For example, for protected animals in Albert National Park in Zaïre (formerly the Belgian Congo), the flight distance of kob antelopes to humans was measured at about 20 yards, whereas elephants started moving away at around 50 yards (Hediger, 1955). When a predator closes in, its prey may suddenly begin to engage in some defensive behavior when a certain *critical* or *fight distance* is violated. For instance, a lion will retreat from an approaching human until its critical distance is reached. Then the lion will turn and stalk the human. Lion tamers use these reactions to control a lion's position in space (Hall, 1966).

Mate distance. In some species, an animal will defend an area around an actual or prospective mate. Condor (1949) noted this behavior in winter flocks of mallards on the Welsh coast. A drake would swim about a body length from a certain female; when another male came too close, the drake would either threaten or swim faster, both of which actions tended to increase the distance between the pair and the intruder. Condor observed similar behavior in flocks of puffins, razorbills, and guillemots gathered beneath their breeding cliffs at Skokholm in the Irish Sea.

A more elaborate form of mate distance is seen in the harem defense of red deer stags (Darling, 1937). At rutting times, stags traveled into the home ranges of the hinds and their young. On certain portions of these ranges, the stags herded the females into rutting areas, which they defended by roaring, chasing, and the classic clashing of antlers. Although at any given moment the boundaries of this space were fixed, over time the location and size of the space defended shifted. Since the site of the stag's rutting area varied, the area could not be called a territory; rather, it represented a form of mate defense.

AGGREGATION

Whereas home range, territory, and free space act to increase the distance between animals, other factors tend to draw animals into aggregations. These factors can be either environmental or social. Aggregations often develop on an environmental basis when animals independently approach some feature in their surroundings; for instance, several desert animals may come together at a water hole. Environmental aggregations may also be the product of many animals' avoidance of the same stimulus; for example, a flood may force animals to concentrate on high ground.

Most aggregations are formed on a social basis:[2] animals respond to conspecifics by approaching and remaining in their vicinity. Social aggregations are of two basic types: those in which each individual is "anonymous" and those in which each individual possesses an identity.

ANONYMOUS GROUPS

In many social aggregations, animals respond to each other only as representatives of the species or as representatives of some sex or age class within the species; no differential response is accorded individuals

[2]Some authors restrict the term aggregation to groups formed on an environmental basis. Here, I have followed the alternative practice of using aggregation as a general term referring to all types of groups.

on the basis of previous encounters. Such anonymous relationships often occur in large or in temporary aggregations. Such aggregations include schools of many pelagic fishes, which may number in the millions, and various small transient groups of foraging animals, as may be formed by migrating shorebirds. Anonymous relationships can also characterize groups that are stable and stationary; in mice and rats, an animal may be treated as a member of the local "clan" or as a stranger, but in either case it is not responded to as an individual (Eibl-Eibesfeldt, 1970).

GROUPS CHARACTERIZED BY INDIVIDUAL RECOGNITION

In other social groups, experience establishes differential responses to individuals. Such individual recognition is frequently expressed in terms of dominance; the dominant animal may have priority in taking space, food, resting sites, and so forth. For example, when barnyard hens are first put into a flock, a series of conflicts between individuals ensues (Guhl, 1956; Guhl & Fischer, 1969; Schjelderup-Ebbe, 1938). Through actual fighting or by merely yielding, each hen establishes its position in a stable *dominance hierarchy.* In this hierarchy, a single bird, sometimes called the *alpha* hen, usually dominates all the other flock members; it has first access to food, to dust-bathing areas, and to roosting and nesting sites; it may peck at all its subordinates without having its pecks returned. In similar fashion, a second hen, or *beta* animal, may dominate all in the flock except for the alpha bird. A third or *gamma* hen may dominate all but the first and second birds, and so on until the last bird in the hierarchy, the *omega* hen, which is dominated by all and dominates none. Such an orderly dominance hierarchy, or *peck order* as it is often called in flocking birds, is termed *linear.* In linear-dominance hierarchies, each animal has a rank such that all animals higher in the hierarchy dominate it, whereas it, in turn, dominates all animals of lower rank. Simple linear-dominance hierarchies may be complicated by the existence of *triangles:* for example, in a flock of hens, the bird ranked five may peck at bird six; bird six may peck at bird seven; but bird seven may peck at bird five.

Because subordinate hens almost never resist their superiors, hens have been said to possess a *peck right* hierarchy: superiors have a "right" to peck inferiors (Allee, 1951). It should be noted that this right is not always expressed. Often, little aggression is seen in small established flocks of hens; a hierarchy may not be apparent until the hens are confronted with a limited resource, such as a small pile of grain (Etkin, 1964). In this case, the alpha bird comes forward to feed, and the others generally stay clear. If the alpha bird is removed, the beta animal approaches and monopolizes the food, and so forth.

A mammalian example of a dominance system similar to that of hens is provided by cattle (Bouissou, 1965; see review in Hafez, Schein,

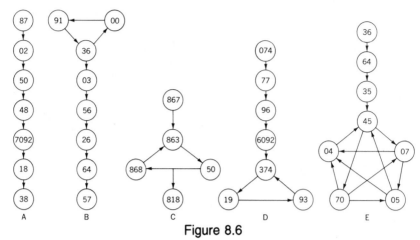

Figure 8.6

Dominance hierarchies in small herds of cows. Most
hierarchies were linear (a); however, triangular and
other more complex relationships were possible (b, c,
d, e). From Bouissou, M.-F. Observations sur la hiérarchie sociale chez les bovins domestiques, *Annales
de Biologie Animale, Biochimie, Biophysique,* 1965,
5, 335. Reprinted by permission.

& Ewbank, 1969). When cattle are introduced into a pen or enclosure,
they immediately establish a dominance hierarchy. This hierarchy is
formed largely through display rather than actual fighting and is quite
stable. In small herds of cattle, the hierarchy tends to be either exactly
linear or linear tending; that is, some triangular relationships may exist
(see Figure 8.6). More complex dominance relationships may also occur:
for example, one animal may be dominated by several subordinates of
its own subordinates. Complex dominance patterns are more prevalent
in larger herds of cattle. In both simple and complex dominance systems, relationships are unidirectional: subordinates retreat from dominant animals "at the slightest threat."

Unidirectional dominance interactions are not seen in all individualized groups, however. Bidirectional relationships may exist between
members of some aggregating species. This form of relationship was
first described by Masure and Allee (1934b) in the domestic pigeon. In
a given conflict between a pair of these pigeons, one would peck and
the other would retreat; however, within minutes, hours, or days, their
relationship typically became reversed. Over a series of agonistic encounters, one of the pair would usually be the winner. Masure and Allee
used the term *peck dominance* to describe this relationship (1934a,
1934b).

Under these conditions, one cannot predict with certainty the result of any contact between two birds; after observation for several days, one can, however, predict with much certainty which of the birds will retreat most often. The individual which stands his ground most frequently is considered the dominant member of that particular contact pair [1934b, p. 389–390].

Although a few pairs in each flock showed the contrasting unidirectional peck-right relationship, the interactions among most animals were bidirectional; and the resulting dominance hierarchy was one not of absolute but of relative ranks.

In some species, an individual's dominance status can vary with the location of the individual's group. For example, in a study of Stellar's jays in a California park, dominance hierarchies were observed when sunflower seeds were left on picnic tables (Brown, 1963). Dominant males typically flew directly to the table and filled their mouths and bills with seeds for storage. These animals frequently supplanted any subordinates that were too close or that were in their path. Subordinate jays would usually land in a nearby tree and wait until only a few, if any, dominant birds were present; they would then approach to collect their seeds. Status in this hierarchy varied according to the locus of the feeding site: the closer the picnic table was to an individual jay's summer breeding territory, the higher was the jay's rank. However, males generally dominated females; only in winter did local females often prevail over distant males.

BEHAVIORAL SYNCHRONY

Social animals do more than maintain proximity and stand in some status relationship; frequently they engage in the same behavior at the same time. *Behavioral synchrony* can be seen in its extreme form in large schools of marine fish such as herring, menhaden, or mullet. In such schools, fish maintain parallel orientation and almost constant interindividual spacing. As the school changes direction, all its members veer together, sometimes creating "the illusion of a huge single animal moving in a sinuous path through the water" (Shaw, 1962, p. 128).

In other cases of synchrony, members of groups may not show such virtually identical responses, but they may engage in the same general type of behavior. For example, a pack of wolves may travel, stop to rest, hunt, kill, feed, rest, and feed again together (Mech, 1970). Each individual does not engage in identical responses simultaneously; instead, the activity of each individual at any given moment tends to be composed of the same set of behaviors.

The degree of behavioral synchrony engaged in by a species may be examined experimentally. For example, Crook (1961) compared synchronization of behavior in small flocks of captive weaver finches, *Quelea quelea quelea* and *Euplectes afra.* The behavior of these birds was categorized as hopping, flying, sitting alert, sitting drowsily, preening, or washing. At fixed intervals during test periods, the number of flock members engaged in each of these activities was counted. *Quelea* showed a high degree of synchrony: at any given moment most, if not all, birds tended to be performing the same type of behavior. *Euplectes afra* showed a lesser degree of synchrony: flock members frequently showed several types of behaviors at the same time, although there was a tendency for the flock to be engaged in only one or two of these types of activity at a given time.

Synchronization can occur between members of two species. For example, when golden-breasted waxbills and red-cheeked cordon bleus were held in the same cage, they tended to fly, feed, and clump together synchronously (Evans & Patterson, 1971). Similar synchronization of behavior in mixed flocks of weaver finches was observed in the field.

Two factors that have been long held to contribute to synchronization are *social facilitation* and the *following reaction* (Crook, 1961; Evans & Patterson, 1971; Lorenz, 1937a; Nice, 1943). Social facilitation has usually been defined as the duplication of the response of one animal by another. The classic study of social facilitation is Bayer's experiment in 1929 (cited by Harlow, 1932) on the domestic hen. Isolated hens were first fed to satiation. Then a second hungry bird was introduced and allowed to feed. The original hens began to eat again, consuming on the average a third as much as they had initially.

In the *following reaction,* one animal follows another and thus moves with it. The following reaction may be considered a class of socially facilitated behavior. (For a different viewpoint, see Crook, 1961.) Following reactions are easily seen when flocks of certain birds, such as water pipits, follow the course of the first bird in taking flight.

Another factor producing behavioral synchrony in social groups of some species is *leadership.* Leadership exists when one or more individuals characteristically determine for the rest of the group the direction of travel and/or the selection, site, and duration of activities. For instance, the movements of herds of Grey's zebra are usually controlled by the alpha mare in the dominance hierarchy (Klingel, 1967).

THE ADAPTIVE SIGNIFICANCE OF SOCIAL BEHAVIOR

As we study the vertebrates, again and again we encounter such socially defined phenomena as exclusive home ranges, territories, individual and mate distances, anonymous groups, and groups characterized by individual recognition. Why have such forms of social relationships evolved so many times? The answer to this question is both simple and complex. The answer is simple in that we know that these basic forms of behavior have generally evolved because, in the history of a species, animals that tended to display such social behaviors enjoyed a selective advantage because they were better adapted to survive and produce young. This adaptation must have been heritable, and natural selection thus favored the genetic material associated with the advantageous social behavior.

Unfortunately, the simple answer that some basic form of social behavior exists because natural selection has favored its expression is not satisfactory. Even though we accept this general premise, we still haven't explained the exact reasons why this particular form of social behavior is advantageous. Discovering these reasons may be a complex matter, often made more difficult by a lack of relevant information. To illustrate the investigation of adaptation, let's turn to two of the most intensively examined areas of social behavior: territoriality and colonial breeding dispersions. These areas exemplify both the complexity and the methods characteristic of the study of adaptation.

THE FUNCTIONS OF TERRITORIALITY

Consider the savannah sparrow, a common North American finch. This sparrow establishes combined mating, rearing, and feeding territories each spring. McLaren (1972) has argued that the primary advantage to the possession of territory in songbirds such as the savannah sparrow is the polygyny that results when a male attracts and mates with more than one female. This polygyny can result in a great increase in the number of offspring for a territory-holding male. McLaren feels that this factor alone can account for much of the selection that expresses itself in territoriality. McLaren's argument is reasonable, but it does not immediately convince all students of avian territoriality. Their hesitancy in accepting his argument stems in part from the fact that we can demonstrate that the possession of a territory does many other things for the male savannah sparrow: it gives him a place to attract females, mate, feed, help rear his young, hide, maintain his distance from conspecifics, and so forth. However, we cannot easily tell which of these functions are incidental and which are critical to evolution and maintenance of territoriality. In other words, the *immediate functions,* or direct consequences, of territoriality must be distinguished from its *adaptive functions,* the consequences that enable the territory holder to reproduce better.

In order to establish that some immediate consequence of a behavior is adaptive, it is necessary to demonstrate clearly that this consequence contributes to the ability of an individual to survive and reproduce successfully. Therefore, in order to substantiate McLaren's view that an important adaptive function of territoriality in songbirds is polygyny, it will be necessary to determine how frequently polygyny occurs in different species and to predict how this polygyny should affect the distribution of genetic materials. If polygyny is relatively common and demonstrably yields increased reproductive potential for its practitioners, we will have compelling evidence that polygyny serves as a factor in the evolution and maintenance of songbird territoriality. Although this relationship seems to hold true for some songbirds, such as the savannah sparrow, precise observational studies of many additional species will be necessary in order to thoroughly document McLaren's case.

Other types of territorial behavior may have different adaptive functions. For example, in the case of food territories, the only logical role these territories can play is to provide exclusive access to a food source or food storage area. It should be noted that access to food may be a factor in the evolution and maintenance of territoriality in any species that defends at least some of its feeding area. This may be so even for often polygynous species like the savannah sparrow; there is no reason why a combined mating, feeding, and rearing territory may not have several adaptive functions.

Unfortunately, it is not always easy to evaluate all the potential functions of territoriality in a species. For instance, in order to be confident that exclusive access to food areas is an adaptive function of combined feeding, rearing, and mating territories, one ought to measure the tolerance of territory holders to intrusion by food competitors, such as young conspecifics from neighboring territories or nondisplaying males. If tolerance for any kind of intruding food competitors were low, this finding would strengthen the argument that exclusive food access could be an adaptive function of territoriality in a species. However, since this study has not been conducted, and many other kinds of relevant observations have never or only infrequently been made, it is not easy to bring the discussion of food defense out of the realm of speculation. The same lack of critical observations makes consideration of other potential functions of territoriality difficult.

Although the general importance of polygyny or feeding in territories that combine mating, rearing, and feeding areas has not yet been clearly determined, it is certain that polygyny plays a key role in arena territoriality. The only logical function of such territories can be to secure mates, and it has been shown that, typically, only a fraction of the males in an arena do all the mating. For example, in one lek of blackcock (male black grouse) in the Netherlands (Kruijt & Hogan, 1967), eight birds held courts that were located at varying distances from the center of the arena. At this lek, the four males whose courts were most centrally located did 85% of the mating, and the four peripheral males did only 15%. The grayhens (female black grouse) were never seen to copulate with the nonterritorial males. This pronounced polygyny is of special interest to the student of social behavior because it implies the existence of strong selective pressures for behavior that secures mates. Such strong *sexual selection* can result in exaggerated sexual dimorphism. For example, the blackcock is named for its glossy bluish-black body plumage; it also possesses a conspicuous white rump, white wing bars, and a lyre-shaped tail. The grayhen, by contrast, is smaller and features a barred brown plumage. The cryptic coloration of the grayhen undoubtedly functions to reduce predation, whereas the male's ornaments and arena behavior can only serve to help secure mates.

Sexual selection is one of the major evolutionary forces operating on social behavior. At least three factors seem to be important in this kind·of selection. The first is *intermale competition.* For example, it stands to reason that a puny bull California sea lion would not be favored in a territorial contest with a full-sized 650-pound (300-kilogram) harem master, and that selection would favor the heavier, stronger bull —at least to some limit imposed by ecological conditions. The sea lion cow, which does not compete like the male, weighs only from 110 to 210 pounds (50 to 100 kilograms) (Peterson & Bartholomew, 1967). A second factor involved in sexual selection is *female preferences.* In many species, females choose their mates from a number of displaying suitors. Their choice can be a selective force and presumably accounts, at least in part, for such phenomena as the bright colors borne by males in many species of birds. *Reproductive isolation* is a third factor. Reproductive isolating mechanisms are behaviors or bodily characteristics that prevent or curtail mating between members of different species. Such mechanisms may be favored in evolution, since interspecific mating is generally disadvantageous: even if a hybrid is conceived in some interspecific cross, it is less likely to survive and reproduce. For example, reproductive isolation is apparently a major function of the distinctiveness of courtship vocalizations possessed by species of birds, frogs, and acoustic insects found in a given area; selection is strong against the evolutionary "wastage" of interspecific matings.

This consideration of sexual selection makes it easier to understand our formal definition of adaptation. An adaptation is a behavior, bodily process, or structure that enhances the probability of successful reproduction. Although adaptations typically yield increased chances for individual survival, they may sometimes endanger the individual in the process of improving its chances for successful mating or rearing young. Sexual selection often appears to produce behavior or structures that make males more prominent and liable to predation. For instance, the

blackcock's arena behavior and plumage must certainly aid its predators.

THE FUNCTIONS OF COLONIAL BREEDING DISPERSION

Just as sexual selection may produce striking colors and showy
displays in animal species, selective pressures for successful rearing may
yield sometimes equally conspicuous *altruistic behavior.* Altruism occurs when parents or kin risk their own survival in order to defend or
care for offspring or relatives. For instance, breeding season is often a
time in which adults in prominent colonies of terns and gulls are vulner-
able to land and aerial predators (for example, Lock, 1973). Yet these
birds have evolved behavior that risks individual survival in these relatively dangerous colonies, since the ultimate selective factor is reproductive success. It should be noted that most forms of altruism do not
stand out like that seen in a colony of noisy seabirds. Parental behavior,
for example, usually comprises rather secretive provision of shelter and
food for the young.

Whereas the contribution of altruistic behavior to reproductive
success may be self-evident, it is often not so immediately apparent why
such social behaviors assume a particular form in one species and a
different form in another. For example, why do gulls and terns typically
nest in colonies, whereas most sparrows do not? Why do shorebirds and
open-country grazing animals form flocks and herds, whereas raptors
and rodents do not? One way of addressing the comparative question
of why a behavior takes a particular form in one taxon and a contrasting
one in another is by the *method of adaptive correlation.* This method
entails studying a number of species in order to find correlations between certain features of their behavior and other factors such as their
social systems, potential predators, habitat, or feeding habits. If correlations are found, they may suggest why it is more advantageous for one
species to behave in a certain way and for another to act quite differ-
ently. As an illustration of the method of adaptive correlation, let's
consider *socioecology,* the study of the relationship of social behavior
to ecological conditions. In socioecology, we often find that many kinds
of animals show similar social relationships under parallel ecological
circumstances. For example, colonies are characteristic of a great number of marine or coastal species, such as gulls and terns, that rear their
young at least in part on land. Since such colonies tend to be located
on relatively inaccessible sites, such as islands or isolated peninsulas, it
seems probable that reduction in predation is a major adaptive consequence of seaside "colonialism" (see Lack, 1968). In contrast to colonial
marine species, most land vertebrates with helpless young nest
solitarily. One major adaptive function of the solitary pattern of nesting
seems to be in keeping nest and food supply in close proximity. This

type of nesting dispersion may also reflect the relative lack of safe sites available inland. Note that such adaptive correlations can merely suggest rationales for why a species favors a particular adaptation. Since the rationales we generate may be imprecise, incomplete, or incorrect, the student of adaptive correlation must be content to live with some degree of uncertainty.

One way to reduce uncertainty about the functional significance of behavior is through direct experimentation on adaptive value. Although the experimental method has been only infrequently employed in the study of adaptation, it can firmly establish the value of some characteristics. For example, a second major adaptive consequence of colonial breeding in sea and coastal birds may stem from the communal defenses often practiced by colonial residents. Although the function of these altruistic defenses as a deterrent for predators seems obvious, until recently no one had ever documented the fact that such defenses reduce predation. This demonstration is important, because if we have some measure of the effectiveness of communal colony defenses we will be better able to weigh the adaptive values of such defenses in maintaining a colonial nesting dispersion in birds.

Kruuk (1964) gauged the effectiveness of colonial defenses in a black-headed gull colony at Ravenglass, in the north of England. Kruuk planted hens' eggs at intervals in lines from outside to inside the gull colony and observed that carrion crows and herring gulls took the eggs more rapidly from outside the colony than from within it. Moreover, when he made direct observations of the black-headed gulls' mobbing of either carrion crows or herring gulls, he saw that the greater the frequency of attacks by the black-headed gulls, the less successful were the egg hunts of the aerial predators. The reduction in egg predation within the colony demonstrated in these experiments indicates that a second major adaptive function of colonies, in at least some species, may be effective communal defense against predators.

Further studies of the Ravenglass black-headed gull colony (Patterson, 1965) have confirmed another advantageous consequence of colonial nesting. The gulls at Ravenglass tended to breed synchronously: that is, there were peak times for such activities as laying and hatching. Direct observation of breeding success showed that the gulls whose behavior was most synchronized were also the most successful at fledging their young. Breeding success outside the peak period was extremely low. The far greater reproductive success of the most synchronized gulls was probably related both to antipredator defenses and to prey density. The effectiveness of the communal defense would have been at its greatest when the largest number of adults were breeding. During this time, the maximum number of potential prey would have also been present. This number may have been more than the predators could exploit, and therefore the very concentration of the prey may have afforded the gulls a better chance of survival.

Studies of seabird colonies such as the one at Ravenglass constitute one of the most extensive and successful attempts to understand adaptive function. Although these studies have shown contrasts in behavior and in adaptive values for different types of colonies, they have also demonstrated that many parallels are present. Overall, it is apparent that the major adaptive function of colonial behavior is reduction in predation.

SOCIAL BEHAVIOR AND ITS ADAPTIVE SIGNIFICANCE

Social behavior varies greatly in the vertebrates. We have attempted to understand some of the reasons underlying this variation through our examination of the adaptive significance of territories and colonies. As we have seen, any complex of social behaviors has both immediate and adaptive functions. Many difficulties in understanding adaptations arise from the fact that each immediate function of a behavior is not necessarily adaptive. In order to establish that a function is adaptive, one must relate the consequence of a particular behavior to individual survival and reproductive potential. Whereas speculation about adaptive function can be easy, it is often difficult to argue convincingly that a given consequence of behavior enhances the individual's chances to survive and reproduce. Careful observation, experimentation, and the study of adaptive correlations can often help us unravel questions about adaptive significance. Unfortunately, even though we may be conservative and logical in our reasoning, and although we draw on all the available evidence, our inferences about adaptive function must frequently remain limited or tentative. We must tolerate such uncertainty, for only thus can we approach the fundamental question of the adaptive function of many forms of behavior.

SOCIALIZATION

9

Mary had a little lamb,
Its fleece was white as snow.
And everywhere that Mary went
The lamb was sure to go.

In many taxa, learning is critical in the development of social behavior: it is only through a program of socialization that an individual animal acquires its full complement of responses to conspecifics. The steps in this program of socialization may be few or many; they may be taken at different times during the life of the organism; and the organism's failure to follow the program at any point may yield impairments in its subsequent social behavior.

In this chapter, we will first consider the development of social responses in young animals. Then we will examine the acquisition of social relationships in adults. Finally, we will discern some parallels between human and nonhuman socialization.

SOCIALIZATION OF THE YOUNG

IMPRINTING

The young of many species of birds are *nidifugous*, which is a sesquipedalian but convenient term meaning that they leave the nest shortly after hatching. Such birds—duck, crane, and shorebird hatchlings, for example—must be *precocial*, or well developed physically and behaviorally. These nidifugous birds must have or rapidly acquire a social attachment to one or both of their parents. The first scientific observation of the way in which the young of many such species acquire this attachment was made by Spaulding (1873). Spaulding noted that as soon as newly hatched chickens could walk they would follow any moving stimulus. Such early social responses could be observed in visually inexperienced chicks only during the first days of their lives. Spaulding demonstrated this phenomenon by placing small hoods over the chicks' heads as they were beginning to break out of their shells and then by removing the hoods at different intervals after hatching. Chicks kept hooded for up to three days would run to Spaulding. However, three chicks subjected to almost four days of visual deprivation did not show a ready social approach; instead, as Spaulding wrote, "Each of these [after having its hood] removed evinced the greatest terror of me, dashing off in the opposite direction whenever I sought to approach it" (p. 289). Spaulding concluded that, before this fear response developed, chicks could form social bonds with a foster parent. As Spaulding reported, "Unreflecting on-lookers, when they saw chickens a day old running after me, and older ones following me miles and answering my whistle, imagined that I must have some occult power over the creatures, whereas I simply allowed them to follow me from the first" (p. 287).

Unfortunately, after Spaulding's promising early work, 60 years passed in which little research was done in this area (see Gray, 1963). This state of affairs was altered by the publication of two papers by Konrad Lorenz in the 1930s. The first was entitled *Der Kumpan in der Umwelt des Vogels* (1935). The second, an abbreviated and extensively revised version of the first, was called "The Companion in the Bird's World" (1937a), a translation of the title of the original. In these papers, Lorenz described a process of socialization that he named *Prägüng* or *imprinting.* The first example of this process that Lorenz cites (1935) was provided by his teacher, Oskar Heinroth. Heinroth had observed the acquisition of unusual social relationships in incubator-reared greylag goslings. When these goslings were exposed to members of our species after their release from the incubator, they quickly adopted humans as parents. In other words, their *filial*—offspring-to-parent—social behavior became directed at people. Therefore, after a brief exposure to a human, newly hatched goslings would follow him; if deserted by him, they would give their distress pipes. Moreover, once having adopted *Homo sapiens,* these imprinted goslings would reject geese as parents: if placed with a pair of geese that had young of the appropriate age, the goslings would flee from these willing foster parents and attach themselves to the first humans they encountered. Thus Heinroth demonstrated that imprinting could result in the exclusive attachment of species-typical filial behavior to a completely species-atypical parent. Although imprinting was the same process that had been studied earlier by Spaulding, Lorenz was apparently unaware of this pioneering investigator's work, and he based his discussion on Heinroth's work and his own.

Lorenz felt that imprinting was distinct from ordinary learning (1935, 1937a, 1937b). Among its distinguishing properties were that (1) imprinting could take place only during a limited "critical period"; (2) once imprinting was completed, there was no forgetting: the process was irreversible; (3) conventional rewards were not necessary in order for imprinting to occur; and (4) certain responses to the imprinted stimulus might appear only later in the subject's life; in other words, a social response did not have to occur during the imprinting process *per se* in order to be subsequently released by the imprinted stimulus.

Lorenz's exposition of imprinting served as an impetus for a great deal of the early research on avian socialization that followed World

War II. (See Sluckin, 1965, for a historical review.) As this research has progressed, much has been learned concerning early social attachment in birds. Let's consider the research of the last 25 years. What techniques have evolved for investigating imprinting?

In studies of imprinting, animals first undergo *training* by being exposed to some stimulus. Depending on the exact procedure followed, the chicks may be able to orient toward, approach, follow, and/or make contact with the training stimulus. For example, one common technique involves placing a young bird in a circular runway. The training stimulus in this runway may be rotated so that the chick has an opportunity to follow it, or it may be simply left stationary so that the chick can approach or make contact with it. Such a study usually includes control animals, which are treated identically to the experimental subjects except that they have not been trained to respond to the experimental stimulus.

Once training is completed, it is considered necessary to conduct a test to determine whether imprinting has occurred. According to Sluckin (1970), five such tests are possible. In the *recognition-at-reunion* test, subjects are presented with the training stimulus. The experimental birds should tend to approach and/or follow it more than the control chicks. In the *choice* test, experimental and control birds are presented with two stimuli, one of which is the training stimulus. The tendency of the experimental animals should be to approach and/or follow the familiar stimulus more often than the controls. The choice test is superior to the recognition test because it can eliminate the possibility that training has merely primed the experimental subjects to respond to any stimulus at all. In the *distress-at-separation* test, the training stimulus is withdrawn from the birds and the experimental animals are expected to emit more species-typical distress calls than the controls. In the *run-to-mother* test, a novel stimulus is introduced, and the experimental chicks, and not the controls, are supposed to retreat to the training stimulus. Finally, in the *work-for-reunion* test, the birds are required to perform some arbitrary response, such as a barpress, for access to the training stimulus. The performance of this response by the experimental chicks should be superior to that shown by the controls. Note that, in all tests, the naïve controls may show some tendency to respond to the training figure simply because it possesses some inherent attractive properties. Therefore, it is the relative difference between the experimental and control animals that is important.

These tests for imprinting measure many of the young nidifugous bird's social responses. If training is successful, these responses become attached to the "parental" stimulus created by the animal behaviorist. In nature, of course, one would expect imprinting to produce a "normally" socialized chick—one that shows species-typical filial responses to its actual parents because of its "natural" first exposure to them.

What have these training and testing procedures told us about imprinting? To what extent have the classic views of Lorenz been confirmed?

Sensitive period. Lorenz's term *critical period,* which implies an all-or-nothing effect (Bateson, 1966), has fallen into some disfavor. Today it is common to regard imprinting as being possible during a <u>*sensitive period*</u> within which the ease of imprinting varies. Such a variation is nicely illustrated by Gottlieb's (1961) study of imprinting as a function of "developmental age"—that is, the length of time the organism has been growing since the start of incubation. Domestic Peking ducklings were trained with a moving male mallard decoy and then were given a choice test between this familiar figure and a mallard hen decoy. Figure 9.1 shows the number of subjects at different developmental ages, their responses in training, and their selection of the familiar

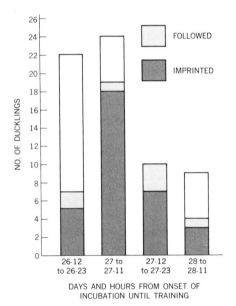

Figure 9.1

Following during training and later test performance in Peking ducklings imprinted at various ages. From Gottlieb, G. Developmental age as a baseline for determination of the critical period and imprinting, *Journal of Comparative and Physiological Psychology,* 1961, *54,* 422–427. Copyright 1961 by the American Psychological Association. Reprinted by permission.

figure in testing. This evidence indicates that on the twenty-seventh developmental day most ducklings tend to readily follow the stimulus during training and that, in subsequent testing, they will ordinarily select the training stimulus. Before and after the twenty-seventh day, there is less following during both training and testing.

The duration of the sensitive period can vary with the experience of the young birds. For example, chicks that were isolated at hatching still showed approach and following after these behaviors had largely ceased to appear in communally reared chicks (Guiton, 1959; Salzen, 1962). Guiton's work suggests that communally reared chicks come to be imprinted on one another and that this imprinting interferes with their socialization to training stimuli.

One factor that may play a role in the termination of the sensitive period is the development of fear responses; indeed, many reports describe the appearance of fear responses to potential social stimuli following imprinting. Perhaps the most extensive study of the ontogeny of fear in nidifugous birds is that of Schaller and Emlen (1961). Chicks of 16 breeds representing eight species served as subjects. Fear responses to a moving stimulus were recorded for at least their first 140 hours of life. These responses ranged from simple retreat to "wild dashing" around the cage, in which the chicks repeatedly collided against its walls. In all taxa, fear responses appeared on the first day after hatching and then tended to increase gradually in intensity until about the fourth day of life. Such fear reactions would be clearly incompatible with filial behavior toward possible training stimuli. However, in studies by other animal behaviorists (for example, Jaynes, 1957), a decrease in early filial responses has been observed even before the onset of overt fear reactions to the training stimulus employed. Therefore, fear responses do not appear to be the sole reason for the termination of the sensitive period, although these responses may certainly interfere with imprinting to the extent that they do occur.

Forgetting, irreversibility, and sexual imprinting. Lorenz's original contention that the social relationships formed through imprinting could not be forgotten and were, in fact, irreversible had two important qualifications. First, on the basis of his own observations, Lorenz noted that, during the critical period, it was possible to shift an animal's allegiance to a new stimulus even after it had already become attached to some other training figure. This type of shift may be possible even near the limits of the sensitive period. For example, Salzen and Mayer (1967) exposed some recently hatched chicks to a blue cloth-covered ball, and some to a green one, for a period of three days. When the chicks were then given a series of choice tests, they showed a strong preference for their training figure. For the following three days, the training stimuli were reversed: chicks that had been exposed to the blue stimulus now received the green, and vice versa. A further series of choice tests revealed that the original preferences of nearly all the chicks had been reversed through their "retraining." The second important qualification made by Lorenz was that imprinting on a parental figure in young subjects did not necessarily fix their adult social preferences; in some instances, the species of the siblings with which an animal was reared determined the species it chose as social objects at maturity. For example, a Muscovy drake fostered by Lorenz directed its sexual behavior at mallards, which were its brood companions. One might say that, in such cases, early experience with a foster parent could be "forgotten." This possibility notwithstanding, Lorenz implied that, in a great number of birds, the species of the parental figure was critical in the establishment of social relationships in adulthood. This generalization requires modification: in the vast majority of nidifugous birds, foster parents do not determine adult social preferences. For example, at the Slimbridge Wildfowl Trust Station in Gloucestershire, many nidifugous species are reared with domestic hens serving as foster mothers. Once adult, "hardly any" of these animals direct their sexual behavior toward hens. Indeed, the Trust's program for propagating rare waterfowl would be in serious jeopardy if this were the case (Bateson, 1968; Fabricius, 1962).

It is true that, in some species of birds, adult social behavior may be directed toward the taxon of the bird's former foster parent. For example, around the turn of the century, Whitman found that passenger pigeons that had been reared by ring doves would subsequently mate with ring doves rather than with members of their own (and now extinct) species (Carr, 1919; Craig, 1908). Craig (1914) reported that blond ring doves, which he had reared by hand from weaning in visual isolation, courted humans. Although through later exposure the birds gradually came to accept female ring doves as mates, they tended to persist in directing their courtship behavior at humans.

In 1962, Fabricius noted that most such examples of *sexual imprinting,* as this form of attachment is often called, are seen in *nidicolous* birds—those that remain in the nest for an extended period of parental care. This lengthy care makes it difficult to assert that imprinting or socialization processes are similar in nidifugous chicks and nidicolous nestlings, for there are many differences in the ways in which these types of young birds interact with their parents. For example, since the nidicolous fledgling takes food from its parents, its social attachment could result from learning based on reward. However, no one has performed the experiment of mechanically feeding these nestlings while independently exposing them to a training figure. Under such conditions, mere exposure to the figure might be sufficient for the development of social attachments, just as exposure alone suffices for nidifugous chicks.

There have been relatively few studies of sexual imprinting. However, these studies do suggest some tentative generalizations. One is that, in at least some species, sexual imprinting may be reversible. For example, Gwinner (1964) found that, although his hand-reared ravens initially courted him, all of them ultimately paired with members of their own species.

A second generalization is that the effects of sexual imprinting may be limited to one sex. Earlier, Lorenz (1935) had indicated that this might be the case in some species. This idea was confirmed by Immelmann (1965) in his experiments with zebra finches. Immelmann planted newly laid zebra finch eggs among the eggs of society finches. The society finches brooded the eggs and usually adopted the resulting zebra finch nestlings, rearing these aliens along with their own offspring. When the successfully adopted zebra finch fledglings were from 33 to 66 days old, they were separated from their foster parents and nestmates. The young zebra finches were then individually isolated until they were about four months old—the age at which these birds become sexually mature. At this point, the zebra finches were given a choice test: they were introduced into a cage that contained a zebra finch and a society finch of the opposite sex. The zebra finch males courted and successfully established pair bonds with the society finch females. In contrast, the zebra finch females, after an initial approach to the society finch males, generally restricted all subsequent responses to the courting male zebra finches. This difference in imprinting is probably related to the fact that the males of these two species are distinctively colored.

Stimulus factors. Lorenz believed that certain training stimuli were more readily acceptable than others as social companions. Moreover, there were limits to the types of stimuli that could serve at all for imprinting. The range of maximally effective or even marginally effective stimuli could be quite narrow. The jackdaw, to use Lorenz's example, was biased to attach its social flocking behavior to stimuli that could fly and were of black color. These attributes are species-characteristics of the jackdaw and its near relatives in the crow family.

Subsequent research has confirmed that species-typical stimuli can be important in releasing the social behavior of young birds. Perhaps the most thorough investigation of the effects of these stimuli is Gottlieb's (1971). In a long series of studies, Gottlieb examined the initial approach and following responses of young nidifugous chicks in a circular training runway. His subjects were chickens, Peking ducks, mallards, and wood ducks. His training stimuli were visual replicas of adults of these taxa and recordings of their various maternal calls. Gottlieb showed that the control of the species-typical visual replicas over filial responses was unimpressive. In a choice test between maternal replicas and species-typical calls emanating from a hidden speaker, about half of the chickens, mallards, and wood ducklings followed the invisible source of sound; only a few chickens demonstrated any following of the visual replica; and, when single moving replicas of various taxa were presented, Peking and mallard ducklings showed no greater tendency to follow their maternal model. In contrast, three of the taxa showed evidence that their species-typical maternal call was more effective than the others in releasing approach behavior.

In a second series of experiments, Gottlieb investigated the ontogeny of responsiveness to the maternal call in mallards. Gottlieb demonstrated that the mallards show a selective response even before they hatch: on day 22 of incubation, the rate of "bill-clapping" in the embryo decreased when the species-typical maternal call was played to the egg. Other calls were ineffectual in lowering the rate of bill-clapping. Further studies showed that the prenatal sensory experience of the mallard could change the usual pattern of development of bill-clapping and could affect the selectivity seen in postnatal social discriminations.

Not only may young nidifugous birds be biased to respond to distinctive species calls; more general stimulus characteristics can also be important in the release of early filial behaviors. For example, visual stimuli that move, flash, or make repetitious sounds tend to elicit more approach and following behavior than their stationary, unblinking, or silent counterparts.

Conclusions. In many species of nidifugous birds, the young may form social bonds during their sensitive period. These bonds can be developed through mere exposure to a stimulus that falls within some range of acceptability. However, certain species-typical stimuli may be especially effective in creating such social relationships. Early attachment to a foster species does not necessarily determine adult social preferences: only in nidicolous birds is such a lasting attachment common. In nidicolous species, unfortunately, the basis for the growth of attachment in the young has not been analyzed.

In sum, Lorenz's original characterization of imprinting was largely accurate. Nonetheless, contemporary ethologists, including Lorenz, now regard the imprinting process as a form of learning. Their attitude rests in part on the acceptance of a broad definition of learning. This definition subsumes all experiential processes that have persisting behavioral consequences for the organism.

SOCIALIZATION OF THE PUPPY

The bond between dog and human is familiar to many of us. In this cross-species relationship, canine and human social responses are redirected: the dog walks with its master just as it would accompany members of a pack (see Scott, 1950), and its human foster family may treat their pet very much like a young child. How do the dog's social responses become transferred from its own species to another? What is the course of social development in mankind's ancient companion?

J. P. Scott and his colleagues (Scott, 1968; Scott & Fuller, 1965; Scott & Marston, 1950) have described a series of developmental periods in the dog. The first three are of interest here. In the *neonatal period,* the puppy's ears and eyes are closed, and its motor abilities are restricted to such responses as crawling and righting itself. Its social repertoire includes approaches made to mother and littermates by means of touch and distress vocalizations—whines and yelps. The *period of transition* begins when the puppy is about 2 weeks of age. The eyes and ears open; the puppy walks, albeit unsteadily, and can lap milk. Elements of more mature social behavior appear: the puppy starts to wag its tail at other animals and to engage in fighting play with littermates. During the *period of socialization,* which extends from about 3 to 12 weeks of age, there are further improvements in sensory and motor functions. For example, the retina assumes adult form and the puppy can manage a sustained though somewhat clumsy running. The puppy shows many new social responses. For instance, puppies begin to form small transient packs, and stable dominance relationships are established. A separation reaction develops: when socially isolated in a strange place, the puppy frequently yelps, whines, or barks; this reaction abates after the puppy is 6 or 7 weeks old (Elliot & Scott, 1961).

It is during the period of socialization that the puppy most easily forms bonds with humans. For example, in a study by Freedman, King, and Elliot (1960), litters of puppies were reared with their mothers in fenced one-acre fields. At intervals, puppies were taken from the fields and exposed to humans during a single week in which daily sessions of play, testing, and care took place. The responses of the puppies varied with their age. Puppies tested at 3 weeks of age soon approached and explored a "passive reclining" man; puppies tested at 5 to 9 weeks showed increasingly intense initial fear reactions. These reactions persisted longer the older the puppies, but approach and contact was seen in all age classes by the third day of exposure. After their introduction to humans, all puppies were returned to their littermates and mothers. At 14 weeks of age, these puppies, as well as unexposed controls, were subjected to two weeks of testing. By the end of the two weeks, the groups earlier exposed to humans showed positive social responses to a handler. Controls showed little, if any, "attraction" to humans, and they tended to resist the leash and to react to a wide variety of stimuli by freezing. The fear responses of these puppies were strong and enduring. As Scott and Fuller (1965) reported, the "puppies were like little wild animals and could be tamed only in the way wild animals are usually tamed, by keeping them confined so that they could not run away and feeding them by hand, so that they were continually forced into close human contact" (p. 105).

As is the case in nidifugous birds, the satisfaction of the puppy's physical needs is not a necessary condition for its socialization. Puppies fed mechanically may be socialized through contact alone (for example, Brodbeck, 1954).

SOCIALIZATION OF THE YOUNG NONHUMAN PRIMATE

The young primate's transformation from a more or less helpless infant to a fully socialized adult is a slow process (see Napier & Napier, 1967). The young anthropoid monkey or ape[1] usually remains in very close contact with its mother. In some species, the infant can cling relatively independently to its mother from shortly after birth; in others, the mother must support her baby during the first weeks of its life. In all taxa, the youngest infants are carried when the social group travels. Among the more "primitive" lemurs, lorises, and their allies, there is more variability in the treatment of the newborn. In some species, the young may be left in a nest or "parked" on a branch (see Jolly, 1972). In others, the young are carried by the mother.

As the weeks pass, infants of many species are "babied" by other members of their social group. For example, in some species, females sometimes called "aunts" (see Hinde, 1965) may approach, touch, hold, carry, groom, or play with the infant. Fathers or other adult males may also play a role (Mitchell, 1969). In fact, in some New World species, the infants are carried almost exclusively by the father.

The infant monkey or ape soon begins to make exploratory ventures away from its mother. At first, the young may be frequently restrained or retrieved. Later, the mother permits her offspring greater freedom. However, if the infant is hurt or endangered, the mother usually comes to the rescue. She can be quite aggressive in defense of her young, vigorously threatening and attacking potential enemies. In some species that have been studied in the laboratory, many of the older infant's departures from mother are caused by maternal rejection. For example, in captive pigtail macaques, mothers may punish an infant's contact-seeking behavior by biting it or shaking its body (Kaufman & Rosenblum, 1969). This rejection behavior peaks at around the infant's seventh month.

The infant's early exploration and play is often directed toward social objects: its own toes or its mother's face are eminently suitable for investigation. Also, the young of many species soon spend more and more time in play with their peers. Certain "games" are characteristic of the growing primate. For example, in "chase," little monkeys run

[1]A brief overview of primate taxonomy is given in Chapter 10.

and climb after one another; the roles of pursuer and pursued may frequently alternate. In rough and tumble play, monkeys wrestle, roll, pummel, and bite, but they almost never inflict serious injury.

Unfortunately, there have been few comprehensive studies of the development of social behavior in primate peer groups. The observations that have been made suggest that interactions with peers are important to the learning of social "skills" and to the establishment of status positions. In other words, the individual learns what responses to make under different social circumstances.

Interference with the social life of a young primate can produce great alterations in its behavior. One such interference is the separation of mother from young. The reaction to this separation varies with individuals and species. For example, Kaufman and Rosenblum (1967, 1969) compared the reactions of young pigtail and bonnet macaques to a four-week separation from their mothers. Three of the four pigtail infants studied showed successive stages of "agitation, depression, and recovery." In the stage of agitation, the infants showed responses such as pacing, searching head orientations, and distress-calling. This pattern changed dramatically in the depression stage: "Each infant sat hunched over, almost rolled into a ball, with the head often down between the legs. Movement was rare except when the infant was actively displaced" (1967, p. 1030). The infants seldom showed social responses, and their play behavior "virtually ceased." After five or six days, the monkeys entered the stage of recovery, in which there was a reappearance of exploration, social responses, and, finally, play. Nonetheless, even by the end of the month of separation, the monkeys did not behave like typical infants. When reunited with their mothers, they showed an increase in proximity-seeking behaviors beyond the level seen preceding separation. The fourth pigtail studied was exceptional in that it did not show the phase of depression. This infant was the offspring of the alpha animal in the dominance hierarchy and was distinguished both before and during separation by frequent interactions with other adults.

When young bonnet macaques were subjected to a similar separation, they showed some agitation but nothing comparable to the pigtail infants' depressive state. In fact, the bonnet's separation reaction is one of the mildest yet observed in the primates. The explanation for its lack of intensity appears to lie largely in the treatment of infants in this gregarious contact species. The infant bonnet is attended by other females from the time of its birth and may be adopted if separated from its mother.

The effects of separation can persist long beyond the reunion of mother and infant. For example, Spencer-Booth and Hinde (1967, 1970) detected changes in the behaviors of young rhesus monkeys for months after a six-day separation from their mothers. Even more severe may be the long-term consequences of repeated maternal separation. Mitchell, Harlow, Griffin, and Møller (1967) found atypical social reactions in 19-month-old rhesus monkeys that had been subjected to weekly two-hour separations from their mothers during the first eight months of their lives. In response to unfamiliar stimulus monkeys, these young rhesus showed more screeching, fear grimaces, social submissions, and coos than did control animals. Moreover, although the control animals often threatened the stimulus monkeys, the experimental rhesus were never seen to do so. Interestingly, the increased "wooing" and submissiveness shown by the experimental animals resembled the behaviors they had shown in the separation reaction that had been so frequently evoked earlier in their lives.

Whereas a temporary maternal separation can have lasting consequences for the growing infant, still greater disturbances in species-typical behavior may be seen when an infant is taken from its mother at birth and reared apart from other primates. The investigation of such effects began innocently enough with the adoption of a new method for producing healthier rhesus infants at the University of Wisconsin (Harlow, 1958, 1959, 1971; Harlow, Harlow, & Suomi, 1971; Harlow & Zimmermann, 1959). The infants were separated from their mothers at birth and were maintained in individual wire cages under a controlled program of care. This procedure successfully reduced mortality and increased average weight gain. Moreover, it confirmed previous observations that such infants would show contact responses to soft cloth: Harlow's infant rhesus clung to the diapers that were left in their cages, sometimes draping them around their bodies like robes, and they protested violently when their diapers were removed for cleaning. On the basis of such observations, Harlow reasoned that the contact "comfort" provided by such soft surfaces might be very important in the development of the primate's "love" for its mother. This hypothesis stood in sharp contrast to the common "cupboard love"[2] theory, which holds that a baby's love for its mother derives from the relief that the mother provides for the infant's physical needs.

To test the importance of contact comfort, Harlow created two types of "surrogate mothers" (Figure 9.2). Both types had a stylized head and a simple tapered body. They differed mainly in that the body of one type was covered with soft terrycloth, whereas the other's was formed of welded wire. Single "breasts" were provided for some mothers of both types: a nursery bottle could be inserted so that its nipple protruded ventrally. Harlow gave eight rhesus infants two surrogate mothers apiece, one of cloth and one of wire. For four of the infant

---

[2]"Cupboard love" is a term used by John Bowlby (1969).

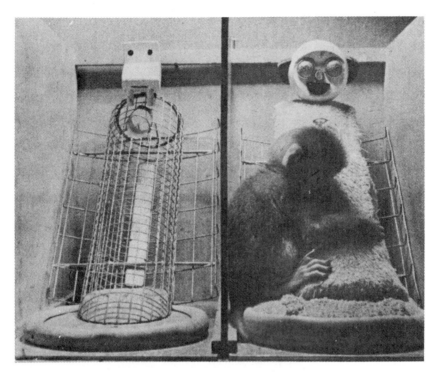

Figure 9.2

Infant rhesus with wire and cloth surrogate mothers.
From Harlow, H. *Learning to Love,* 1971. Reprinted
by permission of Albion Publishing Company.

rhesus, the cloth mother had a breast; for the other four, the wire
mother "lactated." Regardless of which mother was the source of the
milk, the infants soon tended to spend many hours a day in contact with
the terrycloth mother.

Subsequent tests revealed that the terrycloth mothers were more
than a comfortable place to cling. When confronted with a novel mechanical toy, a 2-month-old infant would usually flee to its cloth mother.
Other experiments showed that, if the infants were repeatedly introduced into a novel cage with their cloth surrogate mother, she would
be used as a base of exploration. The infants would at first cling to her
and later make exploratory forays from her. Introduced into a novel
room without their cloth mother, some monkeys "typically rolled into
tight furry balls, screaming in terror" (Harlow, Harlow, & Suomi, 1971,
p. 538).

Although terrycloth surrogates and diapers tell us much about the origin of primate attachment, they cannot replace Mother herself. This fact was compellingly demonstrated by unexpected consequences of Harlow's studies: as the monkeys that were raised alone or with surrogate mothers grew older, it became apparent that their behavior was profoundly disturbed. Harlow, Harlow, and Suomi describe the monkeys that were reared alone.

The subjects . . . showed exaggerated oral activities, self-clutching, and rocking movements early in life, then apathy and indifference to external stimulation subsequently. Individualized stereotyped activities involving repetitive movements characterized many subjects and extremely bizarre behaviour appeared in some. An animal might sit in front of its cage staring aimlessly into space. Occasionally one arm would slowly rise as if it were not connected to the body, and wrist and fingers would contract tightly, in a pattern amazingly similar to the waxy flexibility of some human catatonic schizophrenics. The monkey would then look at the arm, jump away in fear, and subsequently attack the offending object [1971, pp. 543–544].

The behavior of surrogate-reared rhesus also showed severe abnormalities (Harlow & Harlow, 1962).

The serendipitous discovery of such effects was the beginning of a major research effort into primate behavior pathology. Harlow and his colleagues have been exploring many of the variables underlying such disorders and have tried to remedy them with different forms of therapy. Perhaps one of the most significant outcomes of this research is the demonstration of the capacity of peer interaction to prevent the severe consequences of early social deprivation. For instance, when a group of surrogate-reared monkeys was allowed to interact with peers in an elaborate playroom for as little as one 20-minute period each day, they went through the full developmental sequence of rhesus play behavior (Harlow & Harlow, 1962).

SOCIALIZATION OF THE HUMAN INFANT

What is the early course of human socialization? What social interactions are critical in the development of the child? How do different childhood social environments affect adult behavior? Unfortunately, there are no ready answers to these questions. In spite of the extensive research that has been conducted in developmental psychology during recent years, there is a dearth of information about many aspects of socialization. For example, not a single observational study exists that follows the growth of social behavior in a sample of children from 2 to 4 years of age. Moreover, although there are several investigations that trace social development in individual children under 2, these accounts frequently rely on impressionistic evaluations of social relationships or on descriptions of infant behavior by parents, who are hardly unbiased, objective reporters. Nevertheless, keeping such criticism of the literature in mind, a tentative description of early human socialization may be drawn.

The skeleton for this description can be provided by two recent and now almost classic investigations. One is that of Ainsworth (1963, 1964, 1967), who studied the social development of Ganda infants in East Africa. Ainsworth reported that these infants showed four phases in socialization. In the phase following birth, the infant's social responses were directed indiscriminately toward any human. Then, between 8 and 12 weeks of age, the infant entered a second stage, in which he showed a differential social responsiveness to his mother. Shortly after 6 months, the infant entered a third phase, in which he showed a strong attachment to his mother and a diminishing friendliness to strangers. Finally, in the fourth phase, which soon followed and overlapped the third, the child showed attachment to a number of other family members.

The "criteria of attachment" that Ainsworth employed, as well as the age at which they were first recorded in his subjects, are given in Table 9.1. These criteria constitute a classification scheme for many of the human infant's social responses. Ainsworth felt that the attachment expressed through these behaviors was also to a great extent their consequence: many of these behaviors served to initiate and were part of social interactions, and it was through these interactions that attachment developed and was sustained. Satisfaction of the infant's bodily needs was not necessary for the formation of early social relationships; attachment was shown to figures who did not routinely minister to the child's physical requirements but who did play and talk with him. Fathers and siblings, for example, might become attachment figures.

The second recent investigation is that of Schaffer and Emerson (1964) on social attachments in Scottish infants. Schaffer and Emerson used selective separation protest as their criterion for determining the infants' attachment to specific individuals. A sample of parents from a Glasgow district were asked to describe their babies' responses in a number of separation situations, such as when the babies were left in a pram outside a shop. Direct checks indicated that their descriptions were highly reliable. According to these reports, the separation protests of most infants were indiscriminate until they were about 6 months of age: the babies tended to cry when left alone by anyone. Then, in the third quarter of their first year, the majority of the babies' protests began to be selective: separation reactions were more pronounced when specific individuals departed. This selective response was most often first directed to the mother. However, other figures, either from

Table 9.1

Attachment behaviors in Ganda infants. After Ainsworth, M. O. Patterns of attachment behavior shown by the infant in interaction with his mother, *Merrill-Palmer Quarterly,* 1964. Reprinted by permission.

BEHAVIORS	AGE IN WEEKS
Patterns showing "little more" than some degree of selectivity in response to mother	
Differential crying (infant stopped crying when attended by mother and did not when attended by others)	8
Differential smiling to mother	9*
Differential vocalization: more ready and frequent vocal interaction with mother	20*
Patterns indicating concern for mother's location	
Visual-motor orientation toward mother	18*
Crying when mother left the visual field	15
Following mother	17
Patterns displaying active contact-seeking by infant	
"Scrambling" over mother: persistent exploration directed at mother and her clothes	10*
Burying the face on mother's lap	22*
Patterns using mother as a source of security	
Exploration from a secure base (child explored but returned to mother from time to time)	28
Clinging (this pattern was seen when the infant was frightened)	25
Greeting patterns	
Lifting arms in greeting	17*
Clapping hands in greeting	28*
Approach through locomotion	26*

*This estimate is tentative, since Ainsworth identified the pattern only after it was observed.

the start or soon afterward, could also come to release selective protest. The basis for this attachment behavior appeared to lie in the stimulation that these figures provided for the infant. Again, as Ainsworth noted in Ganda infants, relief of the infant's bodily needs was not a necessary condition for attachment; special protests were heard at the departure of "individuals . . . who never participated in routine care activities" (Schaffer & Emerson, 1964, p. 66). For example, the baby might become attached to a preschool sibling who served only as a playmate and/or as a general source of stimulation.

Although many of the infant's behaviors may produce or maintain social interactions, others function to bring the baby into contact with novel or complex inanimate objects. Such exploration of the physical world begins with the young infant's sensory orientations: newborns will stare at a striped stimulus longer than at a plain gray one (Miranda, 1970). Later, this exploration is often facilitated by the presence of attachment figures. For example, in an experiment by Rheingold (1969), 10-month-old babies who were placed alone in an experimental room cried and showed little movement. With the mother present, similar infants did not cry, and they explored freely.

Key attachment figures may also limit the growing child's exploration and play. Following Bowlby (1969), we can attempt to ascertain the relationship of the restraint imposed by mother-figures on the development of independence in the child. As Bowlby notes, child and mother-figure often come into proximity; but the form and frequency of this proximity changes considerably as the child grows. The infant is usually kept within his mother's field of vision or hearing. In the first months of life, the infant can do little to stray beyond these bounds, but he can sometimes produce contact with the mother through his sensory orientations or through his signals. For example, the baby can follow the mother with his eyes or make her come by crying. The older infant can use his improving motor skills to approach and follow his mother and to explore his environment more widely. Should he venture too far, the mother typically restrains or retrieves him. Should he get hurt, the older infant may retreat to his mother, or his mother may come to him. As the child grows, the mother typically allows him to play and explore at successively greater distances from her. However, if the permitted distance is exceeded, proximity-seeking by the mother, and sometimes by the child, results. Gradually, the threshold for proximity-seeking reactions grows higher; the older child may play out of the mother's sight and hearing, and he no longer comes home with every minor injury. The growth of independence continues until adulthood, when proximity-seeking often becomes limited to special occasions or times of great stress.

It should be noted that there are vast individual differences in the course of socialization and in the growth of independence. These differences often reflect the quality of the social interaction experienced by the child. Babies who receive social stimulation when they engage in certain classes of either social or nonsocial responses tend to repeat responses of these types. (For example, see the field data discussed by David & Appell, 1969.) The general level of social stimulation also appears to be important in determining the development of social responses. Indeed, some minimal level of social interaction appears to be necessary for the child's normal development. Unfortunately, this truth has been demonstrated many times: until quite recently, infants in various orphanages and other institutions were unwittingly deprived of extensive interaction with a mother-figure. A study by Spitz (1945,

1946; Spitz & Wolf, 1945) demonstrated the tragic consequences of such severe deprivation. In one institution, which Spitz called the Foundling Home, the social experiences of the infants were severely restricted following their weaning at the beginning of the fourth month: the babies were left socially isolated in small barren cubicles for most of the day. Their major relief from this virtual "solitary confinement" was the attentions of a nurse who was caring for at least seven other infants at the same time. During their first year of life, the infants' performance on a battery of tests fell sharply below that of control subjects. Despite the impeccable hygiene maintained in the institution, these children suffered from a wide variety of diseases, and many succumbed during an epidemic of measles. Even after the infants were transferred to the older children's ward, where much more social stimulation was available, the effect of their early experience proved devastating.

In the ward of children ranging from 18 months to 2½ years, only two of the twenty-six surviving children speak a couple of words. The same two are able to walk. A third child is beginning to walk. Hardly any of them can eat alone [1945, p. 59].

Spitz's work at a second institution, the Nursery, showed that a simple measure could prevent the entire syndrome he called "hospitalism." In this institution, which was an appendage of a women's prison, infants born to inmates were kept and cared for by their own mothers or by other prisoners; the children who remained with their mothers showed no profound behavioral disturbance. However, when a child was separated from a "good" mother, his behavior often began to resemble that seen in the Foundling Home. If the mother was restored to the child, his recovery was "spectacular." However, there was suggestive evidence that some lasting behavioral deficits might emerge following the period of reunion.

SUMMARY: THE SOCIALIZATION OF THE YOUNG VERTEBRATE

The social responses of many infant vertebrates can be released, at first, by a range of stimuli. Soon, however, control of these responses becomes concentrated in a few figures. This acquisition of differential social responsiveness, or attachment, can be the consequence of mere exposure to these figures; social relationships may develop to figures who have never relieved the infant's physical needs. Once an attachment has been formed, the infant will show proximity-seeking for its parental figure; failure to establish contact may produce a vigorous separation reaction. As the animal grows, it becomes increasingly independent of its attachment-figure; however, proximity-seeking may still be seen in times of stress.

SOCIALIZATION OF THE ADULT

What types of social bonds do adult animals form? What processes of socialization are involved in the ontogeny of these relationships? One important process underlying many forms of social relationships in adult vertebrates is the development of individual recognition. Individual recognition is shown by differential social behavior toward particular individuals. Such social relationships are learned. For example, Chapter 8 related that chickens learn their individual status in a dominance hierarchy through a series of agonistic encounters. Two other types of often individualized adult social bonds are of special interest, since they characterize our own species: the bond between parent and infant and the bond between mates.

THE PARENTAL BOND

Parental behavior varies greatly in extent and kind among the vertebrates. In many species, there is no parental care following mating and the release of eggs or live young. On traditional grounds at sea, schools of haddock, cod, and hake spawn and let their eggs drift away; most turtles desert their nests, leaving the young to incubate, hatch, and make their own way in the world. In other species, parental care is limited. For example, the female American alligator constructs a nest, which she may initially defend by hissing, "inflating," and lunging at the attacker with open mouth; but by the time the hatchlings emerge, this maternal defense appears to have waned. The little alligators scatter and must fend for themselves. Assistance from older conspecifics comes only when the young alligator is seized by a predator and gives its species-characteristic distress shriek; if an adult alligator has not been made too wary by poaching and other human interference, it will answer this shriek by attacking the predator (Neill, 1971).

In many groups of fishes and in most birds, marsupials, and mammals, parental behavior tends to be extensive and elaborate. Consider the cichlid fish *Tilapia mossambica*, often called the African mouthbrooder. After spawning, the female takes the eggs and milt into her mouth (Baerends & Baerends-van Roon, 1950). Within this haven, the young develop and become free-swimming. After about ten days, the mother becomes restless, and the fry start to escape from their mobile nursery. At first the mother frequently recaptures her escaping offspring, but later she begins to eject her brood. When all the fry are released, they form a school that follows the mother at a distance. The mother defends them by direct aggression against intruders and by taking the fry back into her mouth.

Although parental behavior may be prominent in the repertoire of a species, the parents may show no differential response to individual offspring. For example, since a 15-cm *Tilapia mossambica* may produce about 400 eggs, the number of resulting fry would make differential responses to individual young impossible. However, many bird and higher mammalian species produce only a few offspring, and parents respond to their young as individuals. This individual recognition may be impressive: when a female Alaska fur seal returns to the rookery to feed her pup, she singles her own out from the hundreds present (Bartholomew, 1959).

The bond between mother and individual young may be established by only a brief encounter. A classic example is provided by goats and sheep. In these animals, the dam's attachment for her young is made within a few hours following birth. If kids or lambs are separated from their does or ewes during this time, the mother will reject her young: she refuses to permit it to nurse and butts it away when it approaches (Collias, 1956). But if the dam remains with her offspring during this sensitive period, the two will usually remain in association until weaning. The kid or lamb tends to stay near its mother and will retreat to her if disturbed; the mother seeks her offspring if it strays (Hersher, Richmond, & Moore, 1963).

The mechanism for the maternal attachment to young in primates is not clearly understood. Females appear to be primed to show maternal responses to infants before they bear young. In fact, "aunt" behavior (discussed in primates earlier in this chapter) may be especially prominent in females that have not yet borne young (Spencer-Booth, 1968; Struthsaker, 1971). Experience with younger babies is not a necessary precondition for the appearance of aunt behavior. When female preadolescent rhesus monkeys that had been reared with peers and/or mothers were presented with an infant, most showed maternal behaviors such as ventral embracing, grooming, and lip-smacking. In contrast, similar male preadolescents typically showed "patterns of indifference or hostility" toward infants (Chamove, Harlow, & Mitchell, 1967).

The disposition to show maternal behavior in primates is usually potentiated each time a female gives birth. Yet both individual recognition of the baby monkey and the fullest expression of maternal care seem to appear only after some days or weeks of interaction. Consider Jensen's (1965) description of the ontogeny of individual recognition in the pigtail macaque. Jensen studied this recognition by first separating a mother from her infant and then placing either the infant or an alien in a cage adjoining the mother's. Initially, the mother's separation protest was reduced when either infant was presented; but toward the end of the first week of the infant's life, increasingly the mother's protests came to be diminished only when her own infant was presented. Jensen also noted that the absolute level of the maternal separation reaction tended to increase during the first two or three weeks of the infant's life. This trend is consistent with data from *Homo sapiens:* maternal love for a newborn develops from impersonal affection to strong individual attachment during the initial months of the child's life (Robson & Moss, cited by Harlow, 1971).

THE PAIR BOND

The link between male and female in a species ranges from promiscuous encounters to lifelong associations. Consider Lack's (1940) five-fold classification of sexual relationships in birds. First, there are the lek species, and others, which meet only at copulation. Second, there are species, such as the hummingbirds of North America, in which the male and female consort for only a few days around the time of copulation. Third, in many ducks, there is a much longer pair bond, persisting until the female lays eggs. Fourth, in many species, the pair bond persists until the brood is reared or until the breeding season is over; most songbirds fall into this category. Finally, some birds mate for the life of the partner; swans and many geese maintain such enduring relationships (Kear, 1970).

Similar pair relationships occur in other vertebrate classes. In apparently all amphibians and reptiles and in many fishes and mammals, male and female pair only briefly at the time of copulation. Yet there may be some selectivity in such pairings: female jewel fish may mate with only the brightest male (Noble, 1938; Noble & Curtis, 1935), and bitches in estrus can be choosy (Beach, 1969). Longer consort, brood, or seasonal bonds may be seen in some fishes and mammals. Pairing for life is rare in mammals, just as it is in birds.

Conspicuous displays often underlie the formation and maintenance of pair relationships. Consider the life bond of the zebra finch of Australia (Butterfield, 1970; Morris, 1954). The bond is established when the female selects one of the several unattached males who court her with dance, posturing, and song. She signals her acceptance by crouching and quivering her tail. From then on, the members of the pair stay in proximity to each other. When inactive, they often rest with their bodies touching, and they may preen one another. When active, they tend to synchronize their behaviors, and both give frequent "contact" calls. The male often begins his courtship sequence. Separation of mates in the laboratory causes both birds to emit a call that is longer and louder than their usual contact signal. The male, but not the female, becomes more active. Presumably, these separation responses help reunite the pair in the natural environment.

THE DEVELOPMENT OF SOCIAL BEHAVIOR

This chapter treats the fundamental question of the development of behavior. We have seen that mere exposure to parent, offspring, or mate can forge strong social bonds. Once such relationships are formed, participants frequently stay in proximity to each other; if they should become separated, protests and searching ensue. Many bonds weaken and break as the young become independent or when the reproductive season is over. In a few species, processes of socialization can result in the formation of lifelong social ties.

HUMANS AND THE PRIMATES   10

There are many approaches to the behavior of humans and their fellow primates. In this last chapter, we will examine the behavior of these "highest" of the vertebrates from the standpoints of the field primatologist and the paleoanthropologist (the student of the evolution of man). First, I will take advantage of many of the concepts introduced in earlier chapters in describing how nonhuman primates behave in their natural environments. Next, we will consider how the behavior of humans came to differ from that seen in other members of the primate order. Finally, I will review the progress that has been made in the analysis of primate behavior.

To introduce our subject, it will be necessary to go into a bit of taxonomy. Who are the primates?

THE TAXONOMY OF THE PRIMATES

The order Primates can be subdivided into two suborders, the Prosimii and the Anthropoidea (see Table 10.1 and Figure 10.1). (My discussion here is based on Le Gros Clark, 1959, 1970; Napier & Napier, 1967; Pilbeam, 1972; and Simons, 1972.) The prosimians, the "pre-apes," constitute the more "primitive" suborder and resemble the earliest fossil primates. Included among the prosimians are the somewhat monkeylike tarsiers, the long-snouted and long-tailed lemurs, the lorises and their allies, and the tree shrews, which bear a superficial resemblance to squirrels. The tarsiers are found in the East Indies and the lorises in Africa and southern Asia. The lemurs and their close relatives are limited to Madagascar and the nearby Cormorro Islands. Here they have evolved without competition from other primates until the appearance of humans in recent times. The tree shrews are widely distributed in southern Asia. Whereas most of the prosimian taxa of mainland Africa and of Asia occupy nocturnal niches, those of Madagascar show a broader range of ecological adaptations.

The suborder Anthropoidea, as its name implies, includes the "manlike" primates (Le Gros Clark, 1959): the New World monkeys, the Old World monkeys, and the hominoids—the apes and men. These three taxa have apparently been distinct at least as far back as the Oligocene age—between 35 and 25 million years ago (Pilbeam, 1972; Simons, 1972). The New World monkeys have evolved in Central and

Table 10.1

Outline of primate taxonomy with some common English equivalents.

ORDER	SUBORDER	INFRAORDER	FAMILY	EXAMPLES
Primates	Prosimii	Tupaiiformes	Tupaiidae	Tree shrew
		Tarsiiformes	Tarsiidae	Tarsier
		Lorisiformes	Lorisidae	Lorises, bush-babies
		Lemuriformes	Lemuridae	Lemurs
			Indriidae	Sifakas
			Daubentoniidae	Aye-aye
	Anthropoidea	Platyrrhini (New World monkeys)	Callitrichidae	Marmosets
			Cebidae	Capuchin, night, and woolly monkeys
		Catarrhini (Old World monkeys, apes, and men)	Cercopithecidae (Old World monkeys)	Baboons, macaques, vervets, colobus monkeys
			Hylobatidae (Lesser apes)	Gibbons, siamang
			Pongidae (Great apes)	Gorilla, chimpanzees
			Hominidae (Man and relatives)	*Australopithecus, Homo*

South America. These arboreal forms are distinguished by the relatively broad separation of their nostrils and by features of their dental and skeletal structures. The gentle and intelligent capuchin, the woolly monkey, and the marmoset are New World monkeys that are often adopted by humans as pets.

The Old World monkeys belong to a single family that includes the baboons, mandrills, and drills, familiar to many of us from zoos, and the rhesus macaque, which serves frequently in medical research. The Old World monkeys are found throughout Africa below the Sahara, in most of southeastern Asia, and in the East Indies. Two Old World species that range farther to the north are the Barbary ape of Morocco and Algeria and the Japanese macaque, which endures the winter snows of the island of Honshu.

The hominoids are represented by the lesser apes, the greater apes, and the hominids. The lesser apes (family Hylobatidae), the gibbons and the siamang, are found in southern Asia and the East Indies. These

Figure 10.1

The primates. (a) Tree shrew; (b) lemur; (c) tarsier; (d) macaque monkey; (e) gibbon; (f) chimpanzee. From Le Gros Clark, W. E. *History of the Primates.* (10th ed.) 1970, British Museum. Reprinted by permission.

fruit-eating forms are *brachiators;* that is, they use their arms to swing and leap through the branches of their forest environment. The chimpanzee and the gorilla of Africa and the orangutan of the East Indies make up the great apes (family Pongidae). Although the gorilla and the chimpanzee are now semiterrestrial, their ancestors were arboreal, just as the nearly extinct orangutan is today. Although the pongids' long arms and other anatomical traits show their affinity with the lesser apes, these groups have probably evolved independently for at least the last 30 million years.

The hominids (family Hominidae) became distinct from the Pongidae around 15 million years ago (Pilbeam, 1972). Although today they are represented (or over-represented) by a single living species, several extinct hominids have been described.

FIELD STUDIES OF THE PRIMATES

Field investigation has yielded many unanticipated findings on the behavior of primates. Perhaps one of the most striking is the great diversity of behavior that can be seen in this order. For example, primate social systems follow a variety of patterns, ranging from rigid linear-dominance hierarchies through roughly "egalitarian" societies to the mutual avoidance that may be observed in solitary animals. Primate species may reside in a number of habitats—for example, deep forest, savannah, arid barren, or the treed or treeless heights of mountains. Different primate species may be specialized to eat leaves, grasses, fruits, or insects, or they may tend to be "opportunistic omnivores."

The particular form of behavior exhibited by a given primate species is related to its ecological niche. Crook and Gartlan (1966) and Jolly (1972) have used ecological criteria to help define several "grades" of primate social organization. Based on these schemes, four grades of primate behavior are proposed here (see Table 10.2). Each of these grades represents a configuration of social and ecological characteristics that is found in a number of primate species.

GRADES OF PRIMATE BEHAVIOR

Grade 1. Only recently have we come to know much about the secretive primate of Grade 1 (see Jolly, 1972; Napier & Napier, 1967). These animals are nocturnal, arboreal, and typically insectivorous. Many are solitary when they forage at night. During the day, some species form sleeping groups.

One distinctive type of social aggregation found in Grade 1 species has been called the *noyau* (Petter, 1962). A noyau, or nucleus, is a concentration of prosimians that is separated from other similar groups by unoccupied but often suitable habitat. For example, noyaus of Demi-

Table 10.2

Grades of primate behavior. Modified from Crook & Gartlan (1966) and Jolly (1972).

GRADE	TIME OF ACTIVITY	VERTICAL NICHE	FORM OF GROUPS	INTERGROUP RELATIONSHIPS	INTRAGROUP RELATIONSHIPS	EXAMPLES
1	Nocturnal or crepuscular	Arboreal	Solitary, small group, sleeping aggregation	Exclusive ranges	Little known	Night monkey, Demidoff's bushbaby
2	Diurnal	Arboreal	Family, harem, small group	Territory, ritualized displays, choruses	Peaceful	Howler monkey, black and white colobus monkey
3	Diurnal	Semiterrestrial	Large structured group	Mutual avoidance	Dominance systems	Savannah baboon, ring-tailed lemur
4	Diurnal	Semiterrestrial	Harem, band, sleeping troop	Avoidance, aggression	Dominance within harem in baboons	Patas monkey, hamadryas baboon, gelada baboon

doff's bushbabies were found at different locations in the rain forests of Gabon, in western Africa, by Charles-Dominique (1972). In one extensively studied noyau, males were seen to possess home ranges of three varieties: "A central" males had large ranges, within which they formed sleeping clusters with females; "B central" males weighed less, had smaller ranges, and only once were captured with sleeping partners; peripheral males were found in a "bachelor club" on the borders of the noyau. The ranges of the A central males were nonoverlapping except in one small communal zone. The noyau thus appeared to represent a form of aggregation involving simultaneous attraction and repulsion among males.

Grade 2. The arboreal primates of Grade 2 are characterized by within-troop harmony and between-troop ritual aggression. Their defense of territory is reminiscent of that shown by birds. For example, Marler (1969, 1972) observed the behavior of black and white colobus monkeys (*Colobus guereza*) along the Victoria Nile in Uganda. In response to intruders, some of the residents of the territory would approach and sit "glaring at their opponents." This behavior was often accompanied by tongue-clicking and sometimes by penile erection—a display behavior in some primate species. If the interlopers still came forward,

an adult male suddenly would begin displaying, leaping noisily from branch to branch, slapping at them as he alighted, and often breaking twigs and dead branches which went crashing to the ground. Great leaps are sometimes performed during this display, the male falling down twenty to thirty feet, with a loud crash. He would then climb back and repeat the performance [1972, pp. 188–189].

After some minutes of such displays, both troops retreated. A second form of conspicuous intergroup behavior was performed not at territorial boundaries but within a troop's territory: a loud rattle-like roar from the males. This distinctive call was first emitted either without obvious cause or in response to some disturbance. Males from neighboring troops would often respond in kind, the "chorus spreading throughout the forest." In contrast to this ritualized sound and fury of exchanges between troops, relationships within troops were peaceful; aggression was infrequent, and social grooming was prominent (see Leskes & Acheson, 1971).

Grade 3. Grade 3 primates are terrestrial animals that may form fairly large troops. Within these troops there are conspicuous dominance relationships, but between two troops there may be avoidance or indifference. The classic illustration of Grade 3 social behavior is that of the savannah baboon, studied by Washburn and DeVore (1961a, 1961b) at the Amboseli Game Reserve in Kenya. These baboons belonged to troops ranging in size from 13 to 185 members. The home ranges of the troops overlapped, and sometimes the troops met at waterholes. In such close quarters there was hardly any social interaction, but smaller troops gradually gave way to larger ones. Within each troop there was a dominance hierarchy governing distribution of space, food, resting positions, grooming privileges, and access to females in estrus. However, the dominance status of the males could be influenced by coalitions: certain adult males might "team up" in an agonistic encounter and allow a coalition member precedence over an otherwise stronger adversary. The dominance hierarchy was reflected in the order of travel followed by the baboons when they moved across open country. First came a few lower-status adult males and sometimes one or two larger juveniles. Then came the adult females and older juveniles. In the center were the most dominant males, younger juveniles, and the highest-status females—those with infants. Bringing up the rear were, first, the remaining adult females and older juveniles and, finally, the remaining lower-status males. In the event of the approach of a predator, the central males would join the peripheral ones and interpose themselves between the predator and the retreating troop.

Grade 4. Grade 4 subsumes only three species—the patas monkey, the sacred or hamadryas baboon, and the gelada baboon. These species are highly terrestrial, often ranging through open country far from the cover of forest. Although each species of Grade 4 represents a different genus, all share one basic element in their social organization, the one-male group or "harem." As might be expected, such harems comprise an adult male and one or more females and their younger offspring. As might not be expected, the social system underlying the harem is different in each species. For example, the patas monkey of Murchison National Park in Uganda, studied by Hall (1965), formed single-male groups that occupied apparently exclusive areas. Within these areas, the adult male of the harem acted as "watch dog" against potential dangers in the savannah and challenged wandering lone males with a series of "contralto" barks. The females were not usually subordinate to the males, and "threat-attack" sequences were rare. Females remained in a group, probably because of their spatial isolation from other patas males.

In contrast to the patas monkey, the mature male sacred or hamadryas baboon, observed in Ethiopia, acquired and maintained his harem by herding females with threatening stares, chases, and bites on the neck (Kummer, 1968). Although the social life of the adult females was restricted almost entirely to the harem, the male and the younger females could engage in interactions with other animals. The harems themselves belonged to larger units called bands. The members of a band tended to move together and to stay near one another when foraging. At night, bands could join to form larger aggregations at rocky cliffs. The bands composing these sleeping aggregations varied in their compatibility. Fights between bands would sometimes prevent or shorten their association.

The one-male units formed by the gelada baboon of the Ethiopian highlands were found alone or in larger herds (Crook, 1966). All-male groups were seen alone, in an "inconstant" association with a harem, or in the herds. Infants and juveniles formed temporary feeding and playing parties within a moving or foraging herd. The composition of herds was fluid; groups of geladas left or joined apparently in response to changes in the distribution and abundance of food. The establishment and maintenance of the gelada one-male group contrasts with that of the sacred baboon. Kummer (1971) closely observed the formation and interaction of gelada harems in a large zoo-like enclosure.

Immediately [after introduction to the enclosure] . . . a male would pair off with a dominant female: the female would present her rear, he would mount her, and she would then groom his cape. From this point on, the female would viciously attack any other female who approached her male or who he sought to acquire in addition to herself. A second female was eventually accepted, but only after the first dominant female had gone through the pair-forming process with herself in the role of the male. Number two had to present her rear, be mounted by female number one, and then groom her [p. 109].

Any gelada females that became members of such harems subsequently acted to prevent contact between their male and outsiders. Furthermore, sometimes most of the females in a harem would join in repelling the advances of an alien male to any female of the group.

The four grades of primate behavior outlined here are provisional. As we learn more about free-living primates, we will improve our understanding of these modes of ecological and social behavior. Perhaps we will want to add some more classes to our behavioral taxonomy. For example, A. Jolly (1972) has already suggested another grade for those arboreal primates that belong to large wide-ranging groups. However, since our knowledge of such species is so limited by the difficulties of discerning and tracking these monkeys as they move through the dense forest, it seems premature to attempt to categorize or characterize these primates.

Additional field work not only will allow us to test the adequacy of this classification system of grades; it may also permit us to tie some apparently exceptional species into this framework. The exceptions are important; they include at least two populations of the great apes, our closest living relatives. Although these animals are semiterrestrial, they fall neither in Grade 3, with its large troops and prominent dominance behaviors, nor in Grade 4, with its harems. One of these exceptional populations is that of the mountain gorilla studied by Schaller (1963) in eastern Africa. These gorillas formed small social groups, of varying composition, that averaged between six and 17 individuals. Within the groups there were dominance relationships, but dominance was rarely expressed; Schaller saw less than one dominance interaction every four hours. He observed that dominance was "asserted with a minimum of action," the most common display involving physical contact being a light tap on the arm or back. Under the leadership of a mature silver-backed gorilla male, the gorillas wandered through their home range, tolerant toward members of their own group and generally "peaceful," if they showed any response toward other groups—hardly in keeping with the King Kong image given gorillas in popular folklore.

The second exceptional population is that of the chimpanzee of the Gombe Stream Reserve (now Gombe National Park) in Tanzania. Van Lawick-Goodall (1968) encountered these terrestrial apes either alone or in small groups, 91% of which had nine or fewer members. These groups were temporary; animals often joined or departed. Despite the transient nature of these associations, the chimpanzees were not neutral toward each other. For example, when two groups met, something like a reunion celebration often occurred: "Males drummed on tree trunks with their feet, shook or dragged branches, rushed along slapping and stamping on the ground, and gave loud 'pant hoots' " (1968, p. 215). Also, long-term ties existed between mother and siblings. Temporary associations frequently included or were totally composed of kin (see Van Lawick-Goodall, 1971).

In addition to the unusually flexible character of their social groups, chimpanzees in the Gombe Stream Reserve demonstrated two distinctive ecological specializations. First, the chimpanzees manufactured tools with which to obtain ants and termites. Larger sticks were broken off for stirring up anthills, and smaller twigs, stems, and stalks were trimmed to use in "fishing" for termites. In this latter operation, the tool was inserted into a termite hill and then slowly withdrawn; termites often bit and clung to the stick and thus were brought out and consumed. Sticks, brandished or thrown, could also be used as weapons. Second, chimpanzees infrequently but actively hunted (see Teleki, 1973). Hunts were performed by lone animals or by individuals acting together. Target animals were usually other primates. Oddly, the chimpanzees pursued and captured young baboons of the same age class that also served as their partners in amicable interspecific play and grooming. The hunt was silent; when the prey was captured, there was an "outburst of vocalization." Following the kill, the meat was shared: the hunters, and any other animals who arrived promptly, divided their prey. Later arrivals picked up fallen pieces, took meat directly, or begged an eater for a scrap. Possessors often honored requests to share. Not once was a fight over possession of meat observed.

Just as some species may fall outside the system of grades, others may have a double classification within the system. This dual classification is possible because certain primates show a great deal of variation in social structure and ecological specialization in different areas within their range. This variation came as a surprise to early field investigators, who implicitly or explicitly assumed that such radically different forms of behavior were not possible within a single species. Consider an exception to a classic example of social organization discussed earlier: the stable, hierarchically organized baboon troops studied by Washburn and DeVore (1961a, 1961b). It was first thought by many that the basic sort of regimented social organization described in this pioneering study was typical of all monkeys and, indeed, of the early ancestors of humans (for example, Washburn & DeVore, 1961b). However, when Rowell (1966) later studied baboons in a habitat of riverside forest and grassland, she found behavior that could be described as more fluid and relaxed. Dominance interactions were rare, males switched troops, troops split and rejoined, and no concentric defensive formation was observed when the baboons traveled. The troops even had adopted as a member a male vervet monkey, a more lightly built and distinctively colored animal. He participated fully in grooming and sexual relationships.

The foregoing accounts of intraspecific variations and grades in primate behavior document the fact that the social structures and ecological specializations of the primates are highly diverse. Three factors underlie this diversity. (For a parallel discussion, see Kummer, 1971.) First, there are *genetic* differences among primate taxa. For example, overlapping troops of savannah baboons and vervet monkeys characteristically display different types of social and ecological relationships. These contrasts in behavior may be largely attributed to variation in *genotype*—the heritable genetic constitution that these primates possess as a result of natural selection and mutation. That is, when we see reliable differences in behavior between populations occupying the same habitat, we can assume that the differences have a genetic origin, keeping in mind that the genotype can have its effect only through a process of interaction with the environment both inside and outside the developing organism. In other words, to say that the differences are genetic is not to say that they are instinctive—that the differences occur independently of the environment (see Chapter 4).

A second class of contrasts in behavior comprises those that may be attributed to *ecological* variables. For example, the fact that vervet monkeys may depend on different foods as mainstays of diet in different areas may directly reflect the fact that the areas do not share many food plants. The environment might thus condition local populations to eat the appropriate foods: it is possible (but has not actually been demonstrated) that the individual vervet might learn what to eat by being rewarded by palatable foods and punished by unpalatable or toxic foods.

The third factor behind the diversity of primate behavior is *cultural*. Groups of primates may display behaviors that are transmitted from one generation to another. Such socially acquired traits are termed cultural, and the entire set of such traits is termed a culture. As might be imagined, it is not easy to establish that a given behavior trait is cultural and not simply the result of an interaction between an individual's genotype and the nonsocial environment. Convincing cases are either those in which the diffusion of a trait through a group can be traced or those in which the actual transmission of the behavior is observed. Some of the best-studied examples of primate cultural adaptations are those seen in the Japanese macaque population on the island of Koshima (see Kawai, 1965). Since 1952, a team of Japanese primatologists has "provisioned" these macaques—that is, supplied them with an artificial source of food. The first cultural acquisition seen was that of potato-washing. In 1953, a young female named Imo learned to wash sand from the potatoes provided her. This trait gradually spread, being most readily acquired by juveniles and close relatives. Some adults never became potato washers; but once a mother began to wash potatoes, she taught the custom to her offspring. By 1962, all members of the troop except the oldest adults and the infants yet to be trained washed their potatoes.

THE EVOLUTION OF THE HOMINIDS

I have omitted one species from the preceding discussion of the primates—*Homo sapiens. Homo sapiens* is clearly another exceptional primate, but the fantastic variability in the behavior of this species makes an exact comparison between it and the other primates rather difficult. What are the critical distinctions between the behavior of humans and that of the prosimians, monkeys, and apes? How did we come to differ so from our fellow primates? What was and is the human specialization, the human niche? An answer to such questions comes out of the past—from the record of bone and stone left by earlier members of the family of men, the Hominidae. The record is incomplete; reconstructing the history of the hominids is like trying to decipher the picture presented by a jigsaw puzzle when only a few of the pieces are available. However, by carefully studying the bits of evidence that do exist, we can begin to envisage the course of hominid evolution. This task actually becomes easier and less speculative with time, since more and more fragments from the past are being found.

Unfortunately, the earliest part of the fossil record is the least complete; there is clear evidence for only one hominid taxon that is more than 5 million years old—*Ramapithecus.*

RAMAPITHECUS

The teeth and jaws of the fossil primate *Ramapithecus* had a human cast: the molars and premolars had grinding surfaces; the canines and incisors must have been small; and the jaws were short and deep (Pilbeam, 1972). Unfortunately, such facial remains are virtually all that have come down to us from the late Miocene and early Pliocene times, from about 15 to about 10 million years ago, when *Ramapithecus* lived in what are now Kenya and India. Yet these few remains have convinced many paleoanthropologists that *Ramapithecus* was an early hominid. Furthermore, the lack of large canine teeth has suggested to some that *Ramapithecus* must have used some other means to fight or feed—indeed, that this primate may have stood upright, his hands free to bear tools (for example, see Pfeiffer, 1969). One bit of evidence supports this suggestion. At the site at which the Kenyan form *Ramapithecus wickeri* was discovered, Louis S. B. Leakey (1968) reported finding concentrations of "broken-up bones" with "depressed fractures of the type usually associated with damage from a 'blunt instrument.' " Leakey believed that these bones, as well as a single piece of lava with battered edges, suggested that *Ramapithecus* was using worked tools to prepare food. Since there is no other indication of tools in deposits of this age, more evidence will be necessary before Leakey's view gains general acceptance. Indeed, it may well be that *Ramapithecus* neither made tools nor stood erect but was a form similar to the contemporary gelada baboon, an animal that possesses specialized grinding teeth for the tough seeds that it picks with its free hands as it sits on the ground (see C. J. Jolly, 1970).

AUSTRALOPITHECUS

After *Ramapithecus,* there are virtually no known hominid fossils for a period of some 5 million years. Then, in deposits of late Pliocene and Pleistocene times, which began about 5 million years before the present (BP), numerous but often quite fragmentary remains of several hominid taxa have appeared. The first of these fossils to be discovered was embedded in matrix from an ancient limestone cave in South Africa. Later, traces of related hominids were found at several other sites in southern and eastern Africa. The interpretation of these fossils —called variously "man apes," "ape men," "submen," or "premen"— has always been a matter of controversy. In fact, debate initially raged over whether the remains were hominid at all and not those of some type of aberrant ape. When after many years paleoanthropologists came to agree that such remains could be assigned to the Hominidae, the point of contention became the relationship of the various fossil forms to each other and to *Homo sapiens*. For a number of reasons, these latter issues have never been completely resolved. For example, since it has often been impossible to date a fossil-bearing deposit with any great precision, one could not say whether one of these hominid forms lived before or after another. Also, paleoanthropologists have differed greatly in their views of the variability that might be expected in a species and therefore have "split" or "lumped" fossil types into a number of often contradictory taxonomic classes.

Despite these incumbent difficulties, the interpretation of the hominid fossils has become less uncertain with passing time. A modern method for accurately dating deposits of volcanic origin has allowed us to pinpoint the age of certain adjacent fossil-bearing deposits. Growing knowledge of Pliocene and Pleistocene fauna in Africa has permitted us to be more precise in dating other fossiliferous beds. Continuing discoveries of new sites and new specimens have given us an increasingly clear picture of the types and the variability of early hominid populations. Today, many paleoanthropologists group the Plio-Pleistocene remains into two general categories, the lightly built or "gracile" hominids and the heavier "robust" hominids.

THE GRACILE HOMINIDS

Australopithecus africanus. In 1924, a geologist who had visited the limestone quarry near Taung, Bechuanaland, brought back two crates of fossiliferous rocks to Raymond Dart, a young anatomist at the University of Witwatersrand in South Africa. One of these rocks showed an interesting endocranial cast—a cast of the inside of a skull. Eagerly, Dart set to work with hammer, chisel, and his wife's knitting needles on a piece of rock that had broken off from the one containing the cast (Pfeiffer, 1969). After several weeks of labor, Dart revealed the front part of the skull of an unusual juvenile primate. As may be seen in Figure 10.2, the teeth and face were rather reminiscent of those of a human child. Although the estimated volume of the skull did not exceed that of an ape's, the shape and configuration of the brain seen in the cast had "ultrasimian qualities"; in fact, the brain showed some closer resemblances to a human's than to an ape's. Dart named his find *Australopithecus africanus,* "southern ape from Africa," and surmised that the Taung child represented a "prehuman stock" that possessed characteristics to be expected of an "extinct link between man and his simian ancestors" (Dart, 1925, p. 198).

Figure 10.2

Face of the Taung child. Author's sketch. After Dart,
R. A. *Australopithecus africanus:* The man-ape of
South Africa, *Nature*, 1925, *115*, 195. Used by per-
mission.

During the next decades similar remains were found at two other
sites in Africa, Sterkfontein and Makapansgat (see Pilbeam, 1972). Together, these finds indicate that between about 3 and about 2.5 million
years ago there lived a short hominid, perhaps 3 feet 6 inches (107
centimeters) tall (Lovejoy & Heiple, 1970) and weighing perhaps 40 to
70 pounds (18 to 32 kilograms). These gracile hominids stood and
walked, although not so efficiently as humans. Their teeth were almost
human: the incisors and canines were small and chisel-like, the molars
had thick enamel and multiple cusps, and all of these teeth were set in
a parabolic arc, like modern man's. Their mean cranial capacity has
been estimated as 442 cc (Holloway, 1970) or 494 cc (Tobias, 1971).
Although these figures suggest that the average cranial capacity of *A.
africanus* was less than that of today's gorilla, its brain was still relatively large for such a small hominoid; the pygmy chimpanzee, of comparable size, has a cranial capacity of only 300 cc (see Table 10.3).

Whether *A. africanus* made tools is a moot question. Several lines
of evidence have been marshaled to suggest that *A. africanus* fashioned
clubs for use in hunting (Dart, 1955; Tobias, 1971). For example, in the
"mountain of bones" studied at Makapansgat, many more distal ungu-
late humeri—the lower bones of the forelimbs of antelope and related
grazing animals—have been found than would be expected on the basis
of the remains of the rest of their skeletons found there. Many of the
condyles—the knobs at the end of such bones—show signs of wear. At
Taung, Sterkfontein, and Makapansgat, skulls of baboons and aus-

Table 10.3

The later hominids. Based on Tobias (1971) and Holloway (1970).

TENTATIVE TAXON	ESTIMATED MEAN CRANIAL CAPACITY IN CUBIC CENTIMETERS*	PROMINENT MORPHOLOGICAL CHARACTERISTICS	SITES	POSSIBLE AGE IN MILLIONS OF YEARS BP
Australopithecus africanus	400–500	Gracile; molars larger than incisors	Taung; Sterkfontein; Makapansgat	3–2.5
Australopithecus robustus	500–530	Robust; powerful grinding teeth, cranial crest	Kromdraai; Swartkrans; Omo Basin (?)	2.5–2
Australopithecus boisei	530	Even more extreme development of chewing apparatus	Olduvai; east of Lake Rudolf	1.6
Australopithecus or *Homo habilis*	656	Gracile; narrow molars	Olduvai; east of Lake Rudolf	2.0–1.5
Homo erectus	935	Pronounced brow ridges; low, thick skull	Tropical and temperate Africa, Asia, and Europe	1.5–1.0
Homo sapiens	1600		Africa and Eurasia before last glaciation	.25–present

*For comparison: gorilla mean cranial capacity 506; orangutan, 411; chimpanzee, 394 tralopithecines have been found that show curious double fractures—exactly such as might have been caused by blows from an antelope forelimb held in the right hand of an *A. africanus* who was facing his victim. Although this last hypothesis (Dart's) about the killers of the primates has found support from an expert in forensic medicine, it has not gone unchallenged. For instance, some of the odd distributions and other characteristics of the bones at the southern African sites may be seen in the dens of contemporary hyenas (see Sutcliffe, 1970). We need further evidence in order to solve the mystery of the early Pleistocene killings and of *A. africanus'* toolmaking ability.

"*Homo habilis.*" Olduvai Gorge, in Tanzania, is part of the Great Rift system that runs from Syria to Mozambique. On the walls of this gorge may be seen a long series of deposits ranging back to early Pleistocene times, the oldest dating from approximately 2 million years BP. Since the 1930s these deposits have been studied by Louis S. B. Leakey, his family, and his associates. In 1960, Mary and Jonathan Leakey (Louis' wife and son) found the mandible (lower jaw) and parietal bones (sides of the skull) of a distinctive type of juvenile hominid. The mandible contained teeth that were nearly human in shape and configuration. The parietals were complete enough that an estimate could be made of the cranial capacity of the skull—675 cc (see Tobias, 1964). In subsequent years, additional bones and teeth were found that were consistent in size with the skull of the large-brained child (see, for example, L. S. B. Leakey & M. D. Leakey, 1964).

Leakey and his colleagues (Leakey, Tobias, & Napier, 1964) have argued that this Olduvai hominid could be distinguished from forms such as *Australopithecus africanus* by its larger cranial capacity, relatively smaller molars, and other features, and they have christened him *Homo habilis*—a name suggested by Dart meaning able, nimble, or "handy" man. Other paleoanthropologists have disagreed and instead consider the Olduvai taxon an *Australopithecus* species, a large-brained type rather similar to *A. africanus* (see Pilbeam, 1972; Simons, Pilbeam, & Ettel, 1969). Regardless of what nomenclature is followed, many stone tools have been found in association with the "able" hominid. Many of these tools were discovered at sealed living sites—occupation "floors" where primitive toolmakers used their tools and left them to be buried and preserved under subsequent deposits of sediments and volcanic basalts and tuffs. For example, a site at the base of Olduvai Gorge yielded tools that Mary Leakey (1966, 1971) has termed choppers, polyhedrons, discoids, spheroids, scrapers, burins, points, anvils, hammerstones, light-duty flakes, and heavy-duty material (see Figure 10.3). In addition, the Leakey party found "a circle of loosely piled blocks" that may represent the oldest known hominid shelter. Similar assortments of crude tools have been recovered from other occupation

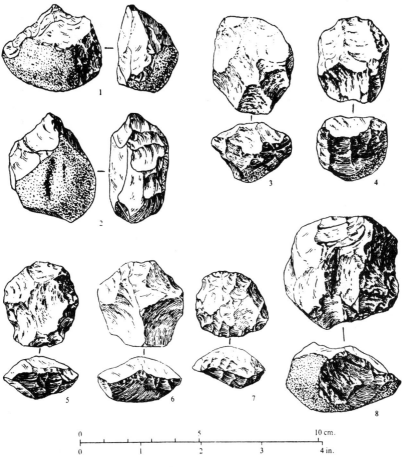

Figure 10.3

Tools from the base of Olduvai Gorge. 1 and 2 are
choppers and the remainder are discoids. From
Leakey, M. D. Excavations in beds I and II, 1960–
1963. In L. S. B. Leakey (Ed.) *Olduvai Gorge,* Vol. 3.
1971, Cambridge University Press. Reprinted by
permission.

sites in the lowest bed of the gorge. Along with these tools are often
found the shattered bones of both large and small animals. These artifacts represent the Olduvan culture, a culture obviously characterized
by toolmaking, meat eating, and the use of "camps"—sites occupied for
extended periods. Since *Homo* (or *Australopithecus*) *habilis* is the only
large-brained form found at the levels of excavation that reveal early
Olduvan culture, many paleoanthropologists assume that he was proba-

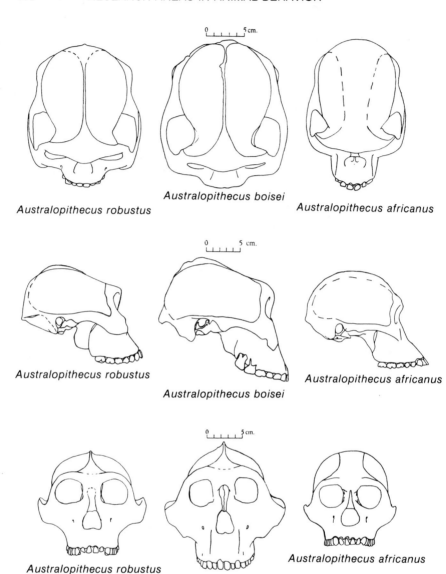

Figure 10.4

Comparison of different australopithecine taxa: Australopithecus robustus, Australopithecus boisei, *and* Australopithecus africanus. From Tobias, P. V. The cranium and maxillary dentition of *Australopithecus (Zinjanthropus) boisei.* In L. S. B. Leakey (Ed.) *Olduvai Gorge,* Vol. 2. 1967, Cambridge University Press. Reprinted by permission.

bly an early African hominid who had specialized to become a toolmaking carnivore.

THE ROBUST AUSTRALOPITHECINES

Australopithecus robustus.   In 1938, a schoolboy named Gert Terblanche found some fossil bones in an outcrop of brecchia—stony debris cemented by lime—from an ancient cave near Kromdraai in the Transvaal. Robert Broom, a paleontologist, recognized these bones as representing a second type of australopithecine. Subsequently, the remains of more than 60 similar individuals were found at another cave site in nearby Swartkrans. Although these hominids resembled *Australopithecus africanus,* they were distinguished by their larger, flatter faces (see Figure 10.4) and by their height and weight: they weighed perhaps 100 to 150 pounds (45 to 70 kilograms) and stood perhaps 5 feet (154 centimeters) high (Burns, 1971). Their skulls featured large molars, deep jaws, flaring cheekbones, and, in most cases, cranial crests—all specializations that permitted powerful grinding and chewing. The name commonly given this hominid, *Australopithecus robustus,* reflects his impressive countenance (see Figure 10.5).

Despite his greater weight, *A. robustus* had a cranial capacity that was probably only slightly larger than that of *A. africanus;* Tobias (1971) believes that the safest estimate that can be made with existing evidence is about 500 cc. Since this capacity clearly exceeds that of the tool-making chimpanzee, it might be reasonable to assume that *A. robustus* made the stone tools that have been found in association with his remains at Swartkrans. However, since traces of a second hominid (*Homo erectus,* described below) have also been found at this site, it is difficult to say who made the tools. In fact, it has been suggested that *A. robustus* was not a tool-wielding meat eater who accumulated the bones of his victims at Swartkrans for later paleontologists to ponder; Brain (1970) has proposed that the *A. robustus* found there may well have been the prey of leopards. One case is particularly convincing: the skull of one robust australopithecine child bears two slightly elongated holes that perfectly match the canines of a female leopard. Whereas the presence of the other 60 australopithecines at Swartkrans is more circumstantial, it is consistent with the theory that *A. robustus* was the prey of early Pleistocene felines, which dragged their victims to the mouths of limestone caves, and that some of the remnants of the carcasses were later washed into the caves to be preserved in breccia.

Australopithecus boisei.   Mary Leakey found the skull of "nutcracker man" on an occupation floor near the base of Olduvai Gorge. As his nickname suggests, this form had powerful jaws: his cranial crest, short deep mandible, and pronounced cheekbones allowed the attach-

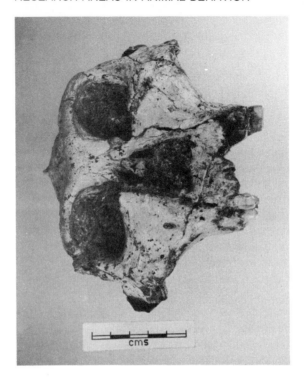

Figure 10.5

Australopithecus robustus. Photograph courtesy of
the Transvaal Museum.

ment of massive chewing muscles (see Tobias, 1967). Although somewhat resembling *A. robustus* in these characteristics, the Olduvai
form's even longer face and larger, broader molars easily distinguish
him (see Figure 10.6). However, in the size of his brain—estimated to
be 530 cc (Tobias, 1967)—and in his height, he was probably little
different from *A. robustus.* Nutcracker man's name is usually formally
rendered as *Australopithecus boisei,* Boise being the name of an early
patron of the Leakeys.

   Although the skull of *A. boisei* was found in association with Olduvan tools, many paleoanthropologists suspect that it was his contemporary *Homo habilis* who actually made the tools, as was noted earlier.
Indeed, some students subscribe to the view that the *A. boisei* skull was
that of a victim of the carnivorous *H. habilis.*

THE AUSTRALOPITHECINE STAGE IN THE EVOLUTION OF MAN

   The australopithecine taxonomy just presented is based on a limited number of samples drawn from only two sources—ancient limestone caves in South Africa and the lower beds of Olduvai Gorge.

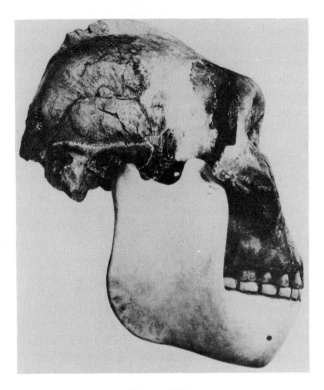

Figure 10.6

Australopithecus boisei. From Tobias, P. V. The cranium and maxillary dentition of *Australopithecus (Zinjanthropus) boisei.* In L. S. B. Leakey (Ed.) *Olduvai Gorge,* Vol. 2. 1967, Cambridge University Press. Reprinted by permission.

Recently, traces of similar gracile and/or robust hominids have been discovered at a number of sites in Tanzania, Chad, Kenya, and Ethiopia (for example, R. E. F. Leakey, 1970, 1971). The new finds range in age from late Pliocene to early middle Pleistocene—roughly from 5 to 1 million years BP. As more remains are found and described (formal description and analysis often take years), we will better understand the evolution of the "southern ape men." It may well be that the earliest australopithecines resembled the gracile *A. africanus,* who seems to have been less specialized than the robust forms. *A. robustus* and *A. boisei* may turn out to represent taxa from different points in time that actually have been sampled from a single evolving lineage. Whatever the case, we can be sure that some australopithecine species or subspecies became transformed into *Homo habilis* or a hominid like him, and that this intermediate type in turn became transformed into the first unmistakable members of our own genus.

Thus, the evidence indicates that our ancestors passed through an australopithecine stage of evolution. Although we can't yet identify which kinds of australopithecines numbered among our forebears, we can suspect that these "prehumans" might have become toolmakers like the early species of *Homo*. In this context, it should be noted that at one of the recently discovered hominid sites—Koobi Fora, to the east of Lake Rudolf in Kenya—have also been found the oldest known tools (Isaac, R. E. F. Leakey, & Behrensmeyer, 1971). Near the few stone-core tools, flakes, and other artifacts were the broken bones of hippopotamuses and antelope. The tools have been reliably dated at 2.6 ± .26 million years BP; this dating indicates that, by this time, at least one hominid taxon had acquired a culture of toolmaking and meat eating. Although the provenance of these tools has not yet been established, the evidence we have for the next stage in the evolution of man enables us to positively link tools and toolmaker.

HOMO ERECTUS

Homo erectus was distinguished by his enormous brow ridges, low, long, thick skull, and thrusting but chinless jaws (see Figure 10.7). He lived in tropical and temperate Europe, Asia, and Africa. The first *Homo erectus* may have appeared 1.5 million years BP; the last, 100,000 years ago. The dates are debatable, since *Homo erectus* was an evolving taxon, and the lines drawn to separate *Homo erectus* from earlier and later species are arbitrary. Specimens of *Homo erectus* are often assigned today to a number of subspecies, which are represented by larger or smaller samples of bones taken from different points in time and space. The earliest *H. erectus* tend to have smaller brains; the 750-cc capacity estimated for one specimen is actually 2 cc smaller than the largest value obtained for the gorilla (Tobias, 1971). Later *H. erectus* had a brain capacity that was less than the average for *H. sapiens,* but the cranial volumes of many individuals fell within the range for modern man.

The stone tools associated with *H. erectus* vary in their technological refinement. An example of rather crude stone industry was discovered at a cave site in Choukoutien in northern China, dating from about 700,000 BP. Here were found numerous skeletal remains of the subspecies of *Homo erectus* called Peking man, his simple stone choppers and flake tools (Figure 10.8), his hearths, and his prey. Most of his prey were deer, but he also took more impressive quarry—rhinoceros, elephants, cave bears, sabertooths, and other *H. erectus*: Peking man was both carnivore and cannibal. Although the exact function of all of his tools is not known, many probably served to shatter the bones and rend the flesh of his prey. A second stoneworking tradition linked to *Homo erec-*

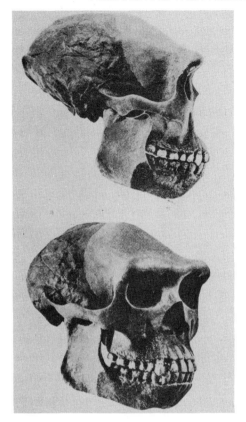

Figure 10.7

Homo erectus. From Le Gros Clark, W. E. *History of the Primates.* (10th ed.) 1970, British Museum. Reprinted by permission.

tus is more advanced: it features hand axes and cleavers. The hand ax may have served as a middle-Pleistocene "jackknife" (Oakley, 1959), a multipurpose tool; the cleavers suggest the butcher's shop. Hand ax industries have been identified at various sites in Africa, Europe, and eastern Asia. Different sites have been dated at from almost 1.5 million BP to perhaps 50,000 BP (Isaac, 1972). During the latter part of this period, *H. sapiens* apparently evolved from at least some populations of *H. erectus.*

HOMO SAPIENS

One view of the evolution of *Homo sapiens* holds that our species passed through two stages. In the earlier stage, humans possessed long skulls, prominent brows, and chinless jaws. One example of such early

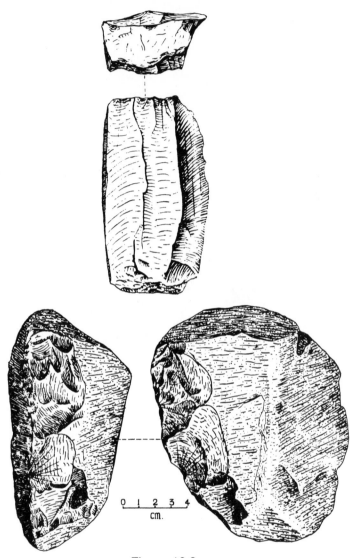

Figure 10.8

Tools of Peking man. From Black, de Chardin, Young, and Pei, *Geological Memoirs of the Geological Survey of China*, Series A, *11*, 1933.

Homo sapiens was that found in western Europe until only 40,000 years ago: Neanderthal man, named after the valley in Germany where his remains were first discovered. In Neanderthal man, "primitive" features were especially exaggerated (see Figure 10.9). Yet the average

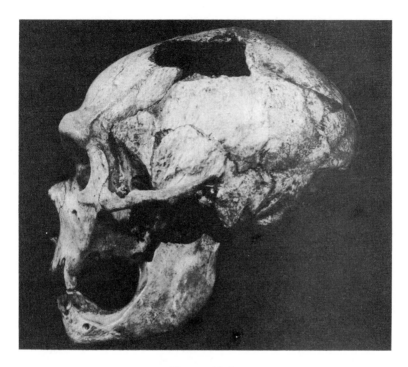

Figure 10.9

Skull of La Chappelle-aux-Saints. Courtesy of Musée
de l'Homme, Paris.

capacity of his skull exceeded that of modern man's, and his last representatives were associated with a rather refined toolmaking culture, the
Mousterian (see Figure 10.10). Mousterian culture was distinguished by
a special technique for striking finished tools from prepared stone cores.
Neanderthal man was also the first *Homo* known to bury his dead,
although, like Peking man, he could also be a cannibal.

The later stage in the evolution of *H. sapiens* is our own. Our origin
was probably in the Near East or Africa: skulls bearing modern features,
recovered from sites in these areas, have been dated at from 100,000
to around 40,000 BP. Shortly after this time, humans in essentially
modern form appear to have invaded Europe, Asia, Africa, and the
Americas. At sites such as Skhūl in Israel and Krapina in Yugoslavia,
intermediates between Neanderthal-like and modern types have been
found; but in Western Europe, the Neanderthals seem to have disap-
peared suddenly. Whether these Neanderthals were swamped by more
numerous *H. sapiens,* were exterminated, like many aboriginal peoples
in America and Australia during the nineteenth century, or were

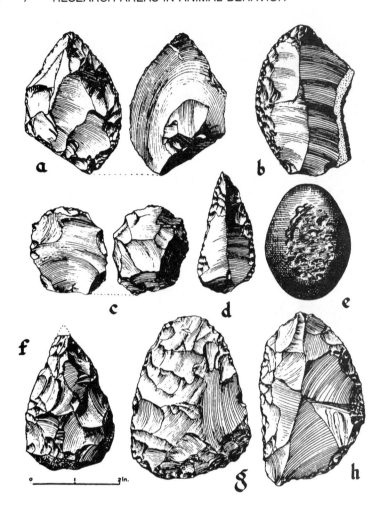

Figure 10.10

Mousterian tools. (a, b) Side-scrapers; (c) Disc-core;
(d) Point; (e) Hammerstone; (f, g) Hand ax; (h) Flake
tool. From Oakley, K. P. *Man the Tool Maker.* (4th
ed.) 1959, British Museum. Reprinted by permission.

pushed into extinction in marginal habitats must remain speculations,
since we lack any evidence of their fate. Associated with the expansion
of modern man into his contemporary range was the advent of advanced Upper Paleolithic cultures. These cultures produced finely
worked and specialized tools, the earliest musical instruments, and
representational art, seen in the naturalistic cave paintings of Spain and
France. The rate of cultural change was sharply accelerated in the

Upper Paleolithic era, and regional differences became pronounced. About 10,000 years ago, civilization began. I must leave the description of this development to the historians.

SUMMARY: DESCENT FROM THE APES

Our descent from the apes involved several steps: we adopted a small-item vegetarian diet; we began to walk and to range out into the savannah; we began to eat meat regularly and make tools. The chronology and even the exact order of all of these events is uncertain, but their end result was the creation of the first men. These men were probably similar or identical to *"Homo habilis,"* creatures intermediate between some *Australopithecus* taxon and *Homo erectus.* Their specialized meat eating, toolmaking, and camping behavior distinguished these earliest *Homo* from their fellow primates. At least some of these first men evolved into *Homo erectus,* a successful hunter and sometime cannibal. Although the volume of *H. erectus'* brain gradually increased with time, his tool kit showed only slow improvement. About a quarter of a million years ago, our own species appeared. Gradually the pace of his cultural development quickened, and more "primitive" *H. sapiens* gave way to thoroughly modern types. The geographical expansion of modern man coincided with the appearance of advanced, diversified, and regional toolmaking cultures.

THE ANALYSIS OF PRIMATE BEHAVIOR

The first part of this chapter reviewed several grades of primate behavior, indicating that the great variation in behavior represented by these grades and by exceptional primate species was the result of three basic causes: genetic differences, ecological contrasts, and culture. The second part of this chapter considered the taxon in which the cultural cause of behavior had become the most prominent: the hominids. Using the methods of the paleoanthropologist, we traced the behavioral evolution of humans and near-humans through the fragmentary record that comes down to us from the past. In this last respect, the hominids are unique: no other group has left such a chronicle of cultural evolution.

This chapter has emphasized the fundamental question of the evolution of behavior, illustrating the kinds of inferences that can be made from bones and artifacts in the case of our taxonomic family. Because of the durability of cultural products such as stone tools and campsites, we enjoy a special advantage in our study of the evolution of humans.

This chapter demonstrated that the later hominids were distinct from the other primates in their specialized carnivorous nature and in the elaboration of their cultures. For these reasons, and because of the diversity of primate behavior, one cannot readily generalize from the other primates to humans or even from one primate to another. Instead, each species has to be studied in its own right. However, we can expect to find parallels in the behavior of different species, just as our own species shares—although to a limited extent—the talents of hunting and toolmaking with the chimpanzee.

Any discussion comparing the behaviors of species, however, brings us to the fundamental question of the limits involved. Anyone who reads popular or scholarly works on animal behavior soon notices that many writers assume that the conclusions drawn from the study of the "lower" vertebrates or mammals must surely be valid for the "higher" mammals, including the primates. Many animal psychologists have written as if they were describing rules of learning and motivation that apply to all animals when, in fact, their theories are based only on the laboratory study of the white rat and pigeon. In similar fashion, classical ethologists have generalized from naturalistic observations of the greylag goose and other birds and fishes all the way to humans, and they have even recommended programs of political action on the strength of their extrapolations. All too frequently, such writers are not familiar with the primate literature, and therefore their treatments of the behavior of monkeys and men have tended to be speculative at best.

In the past, it was possible to ignore the primates, simply because we knew so little about the members of our own order. For example, we had hardly any information about how free-living primates behave in their natural environments, and we lacked adequate data on the limits of the "intelligence" that could be shown by nonhuman primates. Fortunately, the last 20 years have seen a radical change in this situation. Field research, which began with a handful of pioneering investigations in the 1930s and 1940s, underwent a dramatic growth in the late 1950s and early 1960s. Anthropologists, psychologists, and zoologists have all been working in the field, and, as the data presented on field work in this chapter indicate, we have come to know something about primate social organization, aggression, ecological relationships, and many other aspects of behavior.

Complementing the wealth of field investigations are the recent studies that have been made in laboratories and other less sterile experimental environments. In the preceding chapters, we have already considered laboratory investigations that suggest that primates tend to share similar forms of exploration and socialization. Many further important observations have come out of experimental studies. For example, it is clear that chimpanzees can learn a very rudimentary version of the sign language used by the deaf in North America (see Gardner & Gardner, 1969). Also, it has been found that great apes, when given the appropriate materials, can develop the ability to make esthetically pleasing "abstract" drawings and paintings (see Morris, 1962).

The new literature on primates shows us that there are strong parallels among the behaviors of humans, apes, and monkeys. For example, status relationships, cultural and ecological variation, extended infant care, long-term family bonds, and prominent exploratory behavior are characteristics shared by many primates. This literature also demonstrates that the human being is less unique than we believed: he shares with at least the chimpanzee talents for toolmaking, hunting, and the use of weapons, as well as a capacity for language and aesthetic creation. Therefore, in essence Darwin was correct: there is a great deal of similarity between ourselves and our nonhuman primate kin; and although we can never test Darwin's assertion that humans and the primates have similar mental experiences, we can never deny our common behavioral heritage.

But although the human being resembles the other primates in many ways, he is distinct. Consider his intraspecific aggression, his cultural diversity, and his elaborate social systems. No nonhuman primate engages in warfare, with its often fatal consequences; no other primate exploits such a range of ecological niches or forms such a variety of societies; and no primate except the human may belong to a group larger than a band or troop. In this chapter's review of the origin of the Hominidae, we have traced the development of some of the traits that have come to distinguish the human. We have seen that the earliest hominid hunters probably sought other hominids as prey, just as the chimpanzee hunts monkeys and baboons. The australopithecine data suggest that cannibalism is an old hominid custom. In the case of some groups of *H. erectus* and *H. sapiens,* there is no doubt. In any event, man's aggression against man has a long history. In contrast, man's extreme cultural diversity seems to be a rather late adaptation. For 2 million years or so, there was only a slow advance, if any, in the skills of the toolmakers. The last 150,000 years, and particularly the last 50,000, have seen an accelerating rate of social change and an increasing regional culturalization. Even taking into account the regional diversity present in human society toward the end of the last glacial period, some 12,000 years ago, human social systems were not elaborated to the extent we see in the civilized world today. The social organization of preliterate, preagricultural man was probably that of the band or perhaps that of the tribe, as is the case in today's few remaining hunting and gathering cultures (see Lee & DeVore, 1968).

Although we now know something of the history and behavioral characteristics of the nonhuman primates and humans, we still have not specified the mechanisms through which their behaviors are formed. We realize that genetic differences, ecological circumstances, and cultural traditions may all play a role in the development of behavior typical of primate species, local populations, groups, or individuals. But to begin to understand how these causative factors do work, we will have to turn to more observational and experimental studies of primates and humans. We can't merely extrapolate from the principles of behavior outlined by animal psychologists, psychophysiologists, and classical ethologists; we shall have to look directly at the development of behavior in individuals and in groups. It is our good fortune that this work is now under way. Psychologists are attempting to directly modify primate and human behavior and to assess the results of their manipulations after intervals of time. Students trained in the ethological tradition have started to employ standard field techniques in charting the course of primate and human socialization. It is difficult to evaluate or summarize these and other advances in the science of behavior; most of these developments have had their major impetus in the last decade and are happening now.

The end of this chapter, therefore, cannot be written; our work in studying primates remains unfinished. Yet if the progress of the last decades is a sign, and if the human species does not extinguish itself in one final act of intraspecific violence, we will come to understand the behavior of prosimian, monkey, ape, and human being.

REFERENCES

Ainsworth, M. D. The development of infant-mother interaction among the Ganda. In B. M. Foss (Ed.), *Determinants of infant behaviour II.* London: Methuen, 1963. Pp. 67–112.

Ainsworth, M. D. Patterns of attachment behavior shown by the infant in interaction with his mother. *Merrill-Palmer Quarterly,* 1964, *10,* 51–58.

Ainsworth, M. D. *Infancy in Uganda: Infant care and the growth of love.* Baltimore: Johns Hopkins University Press, 1967.

Allee, W. C. *The social life of animals.* Boston: Beacon Press, 1958. (Originally published: *Co-operation among animals.* New York: Schuman, 1951.)

Armstrong, E. A. *Bird display and behaviour.* (2nd ed.) New York: Dover, 1965. (Originally published: New York: Oxford University Press, 1947.)

Aschoff, J. Exogenous and endogenous components in circadian rhythms. *Cold Spring Harbor Symposium on Quantitative Biology. 25. Biological clocks.* Cold Spring Harbor, Long Island: Long Island Biological Association, 1961. Pp. 11–28.

Aschoff, J., Klotter, K., & Wever, R. Circadian vocabulary. In J. Aschoff (Ed.), *Circadian clocks.* Amsterdam: North-Holland, 1965. Pp. x–xvix.

Baerends, G. P., & Baerends-van Roon, J. M. An introduction to the study of the ethology of cichlid fishes. *Behaviour Supplements,* 1950, **1,** 1–123.

Baeumer, E. Lebensart des haushuhns. *Zeitschrift für Tierpsychologie,* 1955, *12,* 387–401.

Barnes, G. W., & Kish, G. B. Reinforcing properties of the onset of auditory stimulation. *Journal of Experimental Psychology,* 1961, *62,* 164–170.

Bartholomew, G. A. Mother-young relations and the maturation of pup behavior in the Alaska fur seal. *Animal Behaviour,* 1959, *7,* 163–171.

Bates, H. W. Contributions to an insect fauna of the Amazon Valley. Lepidoptera: Heliconidae. *Transactions of the Linnean Society of London,* 1862, *23,* 495–566.

Bateson, P. P. G. The characteristics and context of imprinting. *Biological Reviews,* 1966, *41,* 177–220.

Bateson, P. P. G. *Imprinting* (a 16 mm motion picture). New York: Appleton-Century-Crofts, 1968.

Beach, F. A. The descent of instinct. *Psychological Review,* 1955, *62,* 401–410.

Beach, F. A. Locks and beagles. *American Psychologist,* 1969, *24,* 971–989.

Berlyne, D. E. *Conflict, arousal, and curiosity.* New York: McGraw-Hill, 1960.

Berlyne, D. E. Motivational problems raised by exploratory and epistemic behavior. In S. Koch (Ed.), *Psychology: A study of a science,* Vol. 5. New York: McGraw-Hill, 1963. Pp. 284–364.

Berlyne, D. E. Arousal and reinforcement. In D. Levine (Ed.), *Nebraska symposium on motivation.* Lincoln: University of Nebraska Press, 1967. Pp. 1–110.

Bitterman, M. E. Toward a comparative psychology of learning. *American Psychologist,* 1960, *15,* 704–712.

Bitterman, M. E. The evolution of intelligence. *Scientific American,* 1965, *212* (2), 92–100. (a)

Bitterman, M. E. Phyletic differences in learning. *American Psychologist,* 1965, *20,* 396–410. (b)

Bitterman, M. E. Comparative studies of learning in the fish. In D. Ingle (Ed.), *The central nervous system and fish behavior.* Chicago: University of Chicago Press, 1968. Pp. 257–270.

Bitterman, M. E., Wodinsky, J., & Candland, D. K. Some comparative psychology. *American Journal of Psychology,* 1958, *71,* 94–110.

Blest, A. D. The function of eyespot patterns in the lepidoptera. *Behaviour,* 1957, *11,* 209–255.

Bolles, R. C. Species-specific defense reactions and avoidance learning. *Psychological Review,* 1970, *77,* 32–48.

Boring, E. G. *A history of experimental psychology.* (2nd ed.) New York: Appleton-Century-Crofts, 1950.

Bouissou, M.-F. Observations sur la hiérarchie sociale chez les bovins domestiques. *Annales de Biologie Animale, Biochimie et Biophysique,* 1965, *5,* 327–339.

Bowlby, J. *Attachment and loss.* Vol. I. *Attachment.* New York: Basic Books, 1969.

Brain, C. K. New finds at the Swartkrans australopithecine site. *Nature,* 1970, *225,* 1112–1119.

Breland, K., & Breland, M. A field of applied animal psychology. *American Psychologist,* 1951, *6,* 202–204.

Breland, K., & Breland, M. The misbehavior of organisms. *American Psychologist,* 1961, *16,* 681–684.

Breland, K., & Breland, M. *Animal behavior.* New York: Macmillan, 1966.

Brodbeck, A. J. An exploratory study on the acquisition of dependency behavior in puppies. *Bulletin of the Ecological Society of America,* 1954, *35,* 73.

Broom, R. The Pleistocene anthropoid apes of South Africa. *Nature,* 1938, *142,* 377–379.

Brower, J. V. Experimental studies of mimicry in some North American butterflies. Part I. The monarch, *Danaus plexippus,* and the viceroy, *Limenitis archippus archippus. Evolution,* 1958, *12,* 32–47. (a)

Brower, J. V. Experimental studies of mimicry in some North American butter-flies. Part II. *Battus philenor* and *Papilo troilus, P. polyxenes,* and *P. glaucus. Evolution,* 1958, *12,* 123–136. (b)

Brower, J. V. Experimental studies of mimicry in some North American butter-flies. Part III. *Danaus gilippus berenice* and *Limenitis archippus floriden-sis. Evolution,* 1958, *12,* 273–285. (c)

Brower, J. V., & Brower, L. P. Experimental studies of mimicry. 6. The reaction of toads (*Bufo terrestris*) to honeybees (*Apis mellifera*) and their drone-fly mimics (*Eristalis vinetorum*). *American Naturalist,* 1962, *96,* 297–307.

Brower, L. P., Brower, J. V., & Collins, C. T. Experimental studies of mimicry. 7. Relative palatability and Müllerian mimicry among neotropical butter-flies of subfamily Heliconiidae. *Zoologica,* 1963, *48,* 65–83.

Brower, L. P., Ryerson, W. M., Coppinger, L. L., & Glazier, S. C. Ecological chemistry and the palatability spectrum. *Science,* 1968, *161,* 1340–1351.

Brown, J. L. Aggressiveness, dominance, and social organization in the Stellar jay. *Condor,* 1963, *65,* 460–484.

Brown, J. L., & Orians, G. H. Spacing patterns in mobile animals. *Annual Review of Ecology and Systematics,* 1970, *1,* 239–262.

Bryan, J. E., & Larkin, P. A. Food specialization by individual trout. *Journal of the Fisheries Research Board of Canada,* 1972, *29,* 1615–1624.

Burns, P. E. New determination of australopithecine height. *Nature,* 1971, *232,* 350.

Butler, R. A. Curiosity in monkeys. *Scientific American,* 1954, *190*(2), 70–75.

Butterfield, P. A. The pair bond in the zebra finch. In J. H. Crook (Ed.), *Social behaviour in birds and mammals: Essays on the social ethology of animals and man.* New York: Academic Press, 1970. Pp. 249–278.

Carpenter, C. C. Aggression and social structure in iguanid lizards. In W. W. Milstead (Ed.), *Lizard ecology: A symposium.* Columbia, Missouri: Univer-sity of Missouri Press, 1967. Pp. 87–105.

Carr, A. F. *Handbook of turtles: The turtles of the United States, Canada, and Baja California.* Ithaca, New York: Comstock, 1952.

Carr, H. (Ed.). The behavior of pigeons: Posthumous works by Charles Whit-man. *Carnegie Institute of Washington Publication 257,* 1919, *3,* 1–161.

Carr, R. M., & Williams, C. D. Exploratory behavior of three strains of rats. *Journal of Comparative and Physiological Psychology,* 1957, *50,* 621–623.

Chaffer, N. Bower building and display of the satin bower-bird. *Australian Zoologist,* 1959, *12,* 295–305.

Chaffer, N. Australia's amazing bowerbirds. *National Geographic,* 1961, *120,* 866–873.

Chamove, A., Harlow, H. F., & Mitchell, G. Sex differences in the infant-directed behavior of preadolescent rhesus monkeys. *Child Development,* 1967, *38,* 329–335.

Charles-Dominique, P. Ecologie et vie sociale de *Galago demidovii* (Fischer 1808; Prosimii). *Fortschritte der Verhaltensforschung*, 1972, *9*, 7–41.

Cole, M., & Maltzman, I. Editor's introduction. In M. Cole and I. Maltzman (Eds.), *A handbook of contemporary Soviet psychology*. New York: Basic Books, 1969. Pp. 3–38.

Collias, N. E. The analysis of socialization in sheep and goats. *Ecology*, 1956, *37*, 228–239.

Condor, P. J. Individual distance. *Ibis*, 1949, *91*, 649–655.

Conroy, R. T. W. L., & Mills, J. N. *Human circadian rhythms*. London: Churchill, 1970.

Craig, W. O. The voices of pigeons regarded as a means of social control. *American Journal of Sociology*, 1908, *14*, 86–100.

Craig, W. O. Male doves reared in isolation. *Journal of Animal Behavior*, 1914, *4*, 121–133.

Craig, W. O. Appetites and aversions as constituents of instincts. *Biological Review*, 1918, *34*, 91–107.

Crook, J. H. The basis of flock organization in birds. In W. H. Thorpe & O. L. Zangwill (Eds.), *Current problems in animal behaviour*. Cambridge: Cambridge University Press, 1961. Pp. 125–149.

Crook, J. H. Gelada baboon herd structures and movement: A comparative report. *Symposia of the Zoological Society of London*, 1966, *18*, 237–258.

Crook, J. H., & Gartlan, J. S. Evolution of primate societies. *Nature*, 1966, *210*, 1200–1203.

Darling, F. F. *A herd of red deer: A study in animal behaviour*. New York: Doubleday Anchor, 1954. (Originally published: Oxford: Oxford University Press, 1937.)

Dart, R. A. *Australopithecus africanus:* The man-ape of South Africa. *Nature*, 1925, *115*, 195–198.

Dart, R. A. Cultural status of the South African man-apes. *Annual Report of the Smithsonian Institution*, 1955, 317–338.

Darwin, C. R. *The descent of man*. London: Murray, 1871.

Darwin, C. R. *The expression of the emotions in man and animals*. New York: Appleton, 1872.

David, M., & Appell, G. Mother-child interaction and its impact on the child. In A. Ambrose (Ed.), *Stimulation in early infancy*. London: Academic Press, 1969. Pp. 171–190.

Day, M. H. *Guide to fossil man*. London: Cassel, 1965.

DeCoursey, P. J. Phase control of activity in a rodent. *Cold Spring Harbor Symposium on Quantitative Biology*. *25*. *Biological clocks*. Cold Spring Harbor, Long Island: Long Island Biological Association, 1960. Pp. 49–55.

DeCoursey, P. J. Effect of light on the circadian activity rhythm of the flying squirrel, *Glaucomys volans*. *Zeitschrift für vergleichende Physiologie*, 1961, *44*, 331–354.

DeCoursey, P. J. Function of a light response rhythm in hamsters. *Journal of Cellular and Comparative Physiology,* 1964, *63,* 189–196.

Draper, D. C., & Klemm, W. R. Behavioral responses associated with animal hypnosis. *Psychological Record,* 1967, *17,* 13–21.

Driver, P. M., & Humphries, D. A. *Protean behaviour: Systematic unpredictability in interspecific encounters.* Ann Arbor, Michigan: Mental Health Research Institute Preprint *197,* 1966.

Eibl-Eibesfeldt, I. *Ethology: The biology of behavior.* New York: Holt, Rinehart and Winston, 1970.

Elliot, O., & Scott, J. P. The development of emotional distress reactions to separation, in puppies. *Journal of Genetic Psychology,* 1961, *99,* 3–22.

Ellis, M. M. The gymnotid eels of tropical America. *Memoirs of the Carnegie Museum,* 1911, *6*(3), 109–204.

Etkin, W. Co-operation and competition in social behavior. In W. Etkin (Ed.), *Social behavior and organization among vertebrates.* Chicago: University of Chicago Press, 1964. Pp. 1–35.

Evans, S. M., & Patterson, G. R. Synchronization of behaviour in flocks of estridiline finches. *Animal Behaviour,* 1971, *19,* 429–438.

Fabricius, E. Some aspects of imprinting in birds. *Symposia of the Zoological Society of London,* 1962, *8,* 139–148.

Farner, D. S. Circadian systems in the photoperiodic responses of vertebrates. In J. Aschoff (Ed.), *Circadian clocks.* Amsterdam: North-Holland, 1965. Pp. 357–369.

Ferguson, G. Variation and evolution of the push-up displays of the side-blotched lizard, genus *Uta* (Iguanidae). *Systematic Zoology,* 1971, *20,* 79–101.

Freedman, D. G., King, J. A., & Elliot, O. Critical period in the social development of dogs. *Science,* 1960, *133,* 1016–1017.

Gantt, H. B. I. P. Pavlov: A biographical sketch. In I. P. Pavlov, *Lectures on conditioned reflexes.* Vol. I. New York: International, 1928. Pp. 11–31.

Garcia, J., & Koelling, R. A. Relation of cue to consequence in avoidance learning. *Psychonomic Science,* 1966, *4,* 123–124.

Garcia, J., McGowan, B. K., & Green, K. F. Biological constraints on conditioning. In A. H. Black & W. F. Prokasy (Eds.), *Classical conditioning.* II. *Current research and theory.* New York: Appleton-Century-Crofts, 1972. Pp. 3–27.

Gardner, R. A., & Gardner, B. T. Teaching sign language to a chimpanzee. *Science,* 1969, *165,* 664–674.

Gibson, A. N. Experiments on the tidal rhythm of *Blennius pholis. Journal of the Marine Biological Association of the United Kingdom,* 1967, *47,* 97–111.

Gibson, E. J. The development of perception as an adaptive process. *American Scientist,* 1970, *58,* 98–107.

Gibson, E. J., & Walk, R. D. The visual cliff. *Scientific American,* 1960, *202,* 64–71.

Gilliard, E. T. *Living birds of the world.* New York: Doubleday, 1958.

Gilliard, E. T. The evolution of bowerbirds. *Scientific American,* 1963, *209*(2), 38–46.

Gilliard, E. T. *Birds of paradise and bower birds.* Garden City, New York: Natural History Press, 1969.

Gilman, T. T., & Marcuse, F. L. Animal hypnosis. *Psychological Review,* 1949, *46,* 151–165.

Girdner, J. B. An experimental analysis of the behavioral effects of a perceptual consequence unrelated to organic drive states. *American Psychologist,* 1953, *8,* 354–355.

Glickman, S. E., & Schiff, B. B. A biological theory of reinforcement. *Psychological Review,* 1967, *74,* 81–109.

Glickman, S. E., & Sroges, R. W. Curiosity in zoo animals. *Behaviour,* 1966, *26,* 151–188.

Goin, C. J., & Goin, O. B. *Introduction to herpetology.* (2nd ed.) San Francisco: W. H. Freeman, 1971.

Goss, R. J. Photoperiodic control of antler cycles in deer. II. Alterations in amplitude. *Journal of Experimental Zoology,* 1969, *171,* 223–234.

Gottlieb, G. Developmental age as a baseline for determination of the critical period in imprinting. *Journal of Comparative and Physiological Psychology,* 1961, *54,* 422–427.

Gottlieb, G. *The development of species identification in birds. An inquiry into the prenatal determinants of perception.* Chicago: University of Chicago Press, 1971.

Grey, P. H. The descriptive study of imprinting in birds from 1873 to 1953. *Journal of General Psychology,* 1963, *68,* 333–346.

Guhl, A. M. The social order of chickens. *Scientific American,* 1956, *194*(2), 42–46.

Guhl, A. M., & Fischer, G. J. The behaviour of chickens. In E. S. E. Hafez (Ed.), *The behavior of domestic animals.* (2nd ed.) Baltimore: Williams and Wilkins, 1969. Pp. 515–553.

Guiton, P. Socialization and imprinting in brown leghorn chicks. *Animal Behaviour,* 1959, *7,* 26–34.

Gwinner, E. Untersuchungen über das Ausdrucks—und sozialverhalten des Kolkraben (*Corvus corax corax* L.). *Zeitschrift für Tierpsychologie,* 1964, *21,* 657–748.

Gwinner, E. A comparative study of circannual rhythms in warblers. In M. Menaker (Ed.), *Biochronometry: Proceedings of a symposium.* Washington: National Academy of Sciences, 1971. Pp. 405–427.

Hafez, E. S. E., Schein, M. W., & Ewbank, R. The behaviour of cattle. In E. S. E. Hafez (Ed.), *The behaviour of domestic animals.* (2nd ed.) Baltimore: Williams and Wilkins, 1969. Pp. 235–295.

Hailman, J. P. The ontogeny of an instinct. *Behaviour Supplement,* 1967, *15,* 1–159.

Hailman, J. P. How an instinct is learned. *Scientific American,* 1969, *221*(6), 98–106.

Hall, E. T. *The hidden dimension.* New York: Doubleday, 1966.

Hall, K. R. L. Behaviour and ecology of the wild patas monkey, *Erythocebus patas,* in Uganda. *Journal of Zoology,* 1965, *148,* 15–87.

Halliday, M. S. Exploration and fear in the rat. *Symposia of the Zoological Society of London,* 1966, *18,* 45–59.

Halliday, M. S. Exploratory behaviour in elevated and enclosed mazes. *Quarterly Journal of Experimental Psychology,* 1967, *19,* 254–263. (a)

Halliday, M. S. The effects of variation of intertrial interval on exploration of elevated and enclosed mazes. *Quarterly Journal of Experimental Psychology,* 1967, *19,* 264–271. (b)

Harlow, H. F. Social facilitation of feeding in the albino rat. *Journal of Genetic Psychology,* 1932, *41,* 211–221.

Harlow, H. F. The nature of love. *American Psychologist,* 1958, *13,* 673–685.

Harlow, H. F. Love in infant monkeys. *Scientific American,* 1959, *200*(6), 68–74.

Harlow, H. F. *Learning to love.* San Francisco: Albion, 1971.

Harlow, H. F., & Harlow, M. K. Social deprivation in monkeys. *Scientific American,* 1962, *207*(5), 36–146.

Harlow, H. F., Harlow, M. K., & Suomi, S. From thought to therapy: Lessons from a primate laboratory. *American Scientist,* 1971, *59,* 538–549.

Harlow, H. F., & Zimmermann, R. R. Affectional responses in the infant monkey. *Science,* 1959, *130,* 421–423.

Hatch, J. J. Collective territories in Galapagos mockingbirds, with notes on other behavior. *Wilson Bulletin,* 1966, *78,* 198–207.

Hayes, W. N., & Saiff, E. I. Visual alarm reactions in turtles. *Animal Behaviour,* 1967, *15,* 102–106.

Hediger, H. *Wild animals in captivity.* London: Butterworth, 1950.

Hediger, H. *Studies of the psychology and behaviour of captive animals in zoos and circuses.* London: Butterworth, 1955.

Heron, W. The pathology of boredom. *Scientific American,* 1957, *196*(1), 52–56.

Hersher, L., Richmond, J. B., & Moore, A. U. Maternal behavior in sheep and goats. In H. Rheingold (Ed.), *Maternal behavior in mammals.* New York: Wiley, 1963.

Hess, E. H. Ethology: An approach toward the complete analysis of behavior. In R. Brown, E. Galanter, E. H. Hess, & G. Mandler, *New directions in psychology.* New York: Holt, Rinehart and Winston, 1962. Pp. 157–266.

Hess, W. R. *The functional organization of the diencephalon.* (J. R. Hughes, Ed.) New York: Grune and Stratton, 1957.

Hinde, R. A. Factors governing the change in strength of a partially inborn response, as shown by the mobbing behaviour of the chaffinch (*Fringilla coelebs*). *Proceedings of the Royal Society of London,* 1954, Series B, *142,* 306–358.

Hinde, R. A. Energy models of motivation. *Symposia of the Society for Experimental Biology,* 1960, *14,* 199–213.

Hinde, R. A. Rhesus monkey aunts. In B. M. Foss (Ed.), *Determinants of infant behaviour III.* London: Methuen, 1965. Pp. 67–75.

Hinde, R. A. *Animal behavior: A synthesis of ethology and comparative psychology.* (2nd ed.) New York: McGraw-Hill, 1970.

Hinde, R. A., & Tinbergen, N. The comparative study of species-specific behavior. In A. Roe & G. C. Simpson (Eds.) *Behavior and evolution.* New Haven: Yale University Press, 1958. Pp. 251–268.

Hodos, W., & Campbell, C. G. *Scala naturae:* Why there is no theory in comparative psychology. *Psychological Review,* 1967, *76,* 337–350.

Hoebel, B. G., & Teitelbaum, P. Hypothalamic control of feeding and self-stimulation. *Science,* 1962, *135,* 375–376.

Hogan, J. A. An experimental study of conflict and fear: An analysis of the behaviour of young chicks toward a mealworm. Part I. The behaviour of chicks which do not eat the mealworm. *Behaviour,* 1965, *25,* 45–97.

Hogan, J. A. An experimental study of conflict and fear: An analysis of the behaviour of young chicks toward a mealworm. Part II. The behaviour of chicks which eat the mealworm. *Behaviour,* 1966, *27,* 273–289.

Holloway, R. L. Australopithecine endocast (Taung specimen, 1924): A new volume determination. *Science,* 1970, *168,* 966–968.

Hornocker, M. G. Winter territoriality in mountain lions. *Journal of Wildlife Management,* 1969, *33,* 457–464.

Howard, E. *Territory in bird life.* London: Fontana Library, 1964. (Originally published: London: Murray, 1920.)

Immelmann, K. Objektfixierung geschlechtlicher Triebhandlungen bei Prachtfinken. *Naturwissenschaften,* 1965, *52,* 169.

Isaac, G. L. Chronology and the tempo of cultural change during the Pleistocene. In W. W. Bishop & J. A. Miller (Eds.), *Calibration of hominoid evolution.* Edinburgh: Scottish Academic Press, 1972. Pp. 381–430.

Isaac, G. L., Leakey, R. E. F., & Behrensmeyer, A. K. Archeological traces of early hominid activities east of Lake Rudolf, Kenya. *Science,* 1971, *173,* 1129–1133.

Jaynes, J. Imprinting: The interaction of learned and innate behavior. II. The critical period. *Journal of Comparative and Physiological Psychology,* 1957, *50,* 6–10.

Jensen, G. D. Mother-infant relationship in the monkey *Macaca nemestrina:* Development of specificity of maternal response to own infant. *Journal of Comparative and Physiological Psychology,* 1965, *3,* 305–308.

Johnston, W. A. Trends in escape and exploration. *Journal of Comparative Physiological Psychology,* 1964, *58,* 431–435.

Jolly, A. *The evolution of primate behavior.* New York: Macmillan, 1972.

Jolly, C. J. The seed-eaters: A new model of hominid differentiation based on a baboon analogy. *Man,* 1970, new series 5, 5–26.

Kamil, A. C., Lougee, M., & Shulman, R. J. Learning-set behavior in the learning-set experienced blue jay (*Cyanocitta cristata*). *Journal of Comparative and Physiological Psychology,* 1973, *82,* 394–405.

Kaufman, I. C., & Rosenblum, L. A. Depression in infant monkeys separated from their mothers. *Science,* 1967, *155,* 1030–1031.

Kaufman, I. C., & Rosenblum, L. A. The waning of the infant-mother bond in two species of macaque. In B. M. Foss (Ed.), *Determinants of infant behavior IV.* London: Methuen, 1969. Pp. 41–59.

Kaufmann, J. H. Ecology and social behavior of the coati, *Nasua narica,* on Barro Colorado Island, Panama. *University of California Publications in Zoology,* 1962, *60,* 95–222.

Kawai, M. Newly-acquired pre-cultural behavior of the natural troop of Japanese monkeys on Koshima Island. *Primates,* 1965, *6,* 1–30.

Kear, J. The adaptive radiation of parental care in waterfowl. In J. H. Crook (Ed.), *Social behaviour in birds and mammals: Essays on the social ethology of animals and man.* New York: Academic Press, 1970. Pp. 357–392.

Keenleyside, M. H. A., & Yamamoto, F. T. Territorial behaviour of juvenile Atlantic salmon (*Salmo salar* L.). *Behaviour,* 1962, *19,* 139–169.

Kendler, H. H. *Basic psychology.* (2nd ed.) New York: Appleton-Century-Crofts, 1968.

Kilham, L. E. Territorial behavior of wintering red-headed woodpeckers. *Wilson Bulletin,* 1958, *70,* 347–358.

Kimble, G. A. *Hilgard and Marquis' conditioning and learning.* (2nd ed.) New York: Appleton-Century-Crofts, 1961.

King, J. A. Social behavior, social organization, and population dynamics in a black-tailed prairie dog town in the Black Hills of South Dakota. *Contributions from the Laboratory of Vertebrate Biology, University of Michigan.* Ann Arbor: University of Michigan, 1955, No. 67. Pp. 1–123.

Kish, G. B. Studies of sensory reinforcement. In W. K. Honig (Ed.), *Operant behavior: Areas of research and application.* New York: Appleton-Century-Crofts, 1966. Pp. 109–157.

Kleitman, N. *Sleep and wakefulness.* (Rev. ed.) Chicago: University of Chicago Press, 1963.

Klingel, H. Soziale Organisation und Verhalten freilebender Steppenzebras. *Zeitschrift für Tierpsychologie,* 1967, *24,* 580–624.

Koehler, O., & Zagarus, A. Beitrage zum Brutverhalten des Halsbrandregen-pfeifers (*Charadrius hiaticulus* L.) *Beiträge zur Fortpfanzung Biologie der Vögel, mit Berucksicktigung der Oologie,* 1937, *13,* 1–9.

Koford, C. B. *The California condor.* New York: Dover, 1966. (Originally published: Washington: National Audubon Society, 1953.)

Koshtoyants, K. I. M. Sechenov. In K. Koshtoyants (Ed.), *I. M. Sechenov: Selected physiological and psychological works.* Moscow: Foreign Language Publishing House, not dated. Pp. 7–27.

Kruijt, J. P., & Hogan, J. A. Social behaviour on the lek in the black grouse, *Lyrurus tetrix tetrix* (L.). *Ardea,* 1967, *55,* 203–240.

Kruuk, H. Predators and anti-predator behaviour of the black-headed gull (*Larus ridibundus* L.). *Behaviour Supplements,* 1964, *11,* 1–129.

Kummer, H. *Social organization of hamadryas baboons: A field study.* Chicago: University of Chicago Press, 1968.

Kummer, H. *Primate societies.* Chicago: Aldine–Atherton, 1971.

Kuo, Z.-Y. How are instincts acquired? *Psychological Review,* 1922, *29,* 334–365.

Lack, D. Pair-formation in birds. *Condor,* 1940, *42,* 269–286.

Lack, D. *The life of the robin.* London: Witherby, 1943.

Lack, D. *Ecological adaptations for breeding in birds.* London: Methuen, 1968.

Leakey, L. S. B. Bone smashing by late Miocene Hominidae. *Nature,* 1968, *211,* 528–530.

Leakey, L. S. B., & Leakey, M. D. Discoveries of fossil hominids in Tanganyika: At Olduvai and near Lake Natron. *Nature,* 1964, *202,* 5–7.

Leakey, L. S. B., Tobias, P. V., & Napier, J. R. A new species of the genus *Homo* from Olduvai Gorge. *Nature,* 1964, *202,* 7–9.

Leakey, M. D. A review of the Olduwan culture from Olduvai Gorge. *Nature,* 1966, *210,* 462–466.

Leakey, M. D. Excavations in Beds I and II, 1960–1963. In L. S. B. Leakey (Ed.), *Olduvai Gorge.* Vol. 3. Cambridge: Cambridge University Press, 1971.

Leakey, R. E. F. New hominid remains and early artifacts from northern Kenya. *Nature,* 1970, *226,* 223–224.

Leakey, R. E. F. Further evidence of Lower Pleistocene hominids from East Rudolf, North Kenya. *Nature,* 1971, *231,* 241–245.

Lee, R. B., & DeVore, I. (Eds.) *Man the hunter.* Chicago: Aldine, 1968.

Le Gros Clark, W. E. *The antecedents of man.* Edinburgh: Edinburgh University Press, 1959.

Le Gros Clark, W. E. *History of the primates.* (10th ed.) London: British Museum (Natural History), 1970.

Lehrman, D. S. Hormonal regulation of parental behavior in birds and infrahuman mammals. In W. C. Young (Ed.), *Sex and internal secretions.* Vol. 2. Baltimore: Williams and Wilkins, 1961. Pp. 1268–1382.

Lehrman, D. S. Control of behavior cycles in reproduction. In W. Etkin (Ed.), *Social behavior and organization among vertebrates.* Chicago: University of Chicago Press, 1964. Pp. 142–166. (a)

Lehrman, D. S. The reproductive behavior of ring doves. *Scientific American,* 1964, *211,* 5, 48–54. (b)

Leskes, A., & Acheson, N. H. Social organization of a free-ranging troop of black colobus monkeys (*Colobus abyssinicus*). In H. Kummer (Ed.), *Proceedings of the Third International Congress on Primatology, Zurich, 1970.* Basel: S. Karger, 1971. Pp. 22–31.

Lock, A. R. A study of the breeding biology of two species of gulls nesting on Sable Island, Nova Scotia. Unpublished doctoral dissertation, Dalhousie University, 1973.

Loizos, C. Play in mammals. *Symposia of the Zoological Society of London,* 1966, *18,* 1–9.

Lott, D. F. Parental behavior. In G. Bermant (Ed.), *Perspectives on animal behavior.* Glenview, Illinois: Scott, Foresman, 1973. Pp. 239–279.

Lorenz, K. Der Kumpan in der Umwelt des Vogels. *Journal für Ornithologie,* 1935, *83,* 137–213, 289–413. Translated in K. Lorenz, *Studies in animal and human behaviour.* London: Methuen, 1970.

Lorenz, K. The companion in the bird's world. *Auk,* 1937, *54,* 245–273. (a)

Lorenz, K. Über die Bildung des Instinktbegriffes. *Naturwissenschaften,* 1937, *25,* 289–300, 307–318, 324–331. Translated in K. Lorenz, *Studies in animal and human behavior,* Vol 1. London: Methuen, 1970. (b)

Lorenz, K. The comparative method in studying innate behaviour patterns. *Symposia of the Society for Experimental Biology,* 1950, *4,* 221–268.

Lorenz, K. Plays and vacuum activity in animals. In *L'instinct dans le comportement des animaux et de l'homme.* Paris: Masson, 1956. Pp. 633–645.

Lorenz, K. *Evolution and modification of behavior.* Chicago: University of Chicago Press, 1965.

Lorenz, K. *Studies in animal and human behaviour.* Vol 1. London: Methuen, 1970.

Lovejoy, C. O., & Heiple, K. G. A reconstruction of the femur of *Australopithecus africanus. American Journal of Physical Anthropology,* 1970, *32,* 33–40.

Lynn, R. *Attention, arousal and the orientation reaction.* Oxford: Pergamon Press, 1966.

Mackintosh, N. J. Comparative studies of reversal and probability learning: rats, birds and fish. In R. M. Gilbert and N. S. Sutherland (Eds.), *Animal discrimination learning.* New York: Academic Press, 1969. Pp. 137–162.

Mackintosh, N. J., & Cauty, A. Spatial reversal learning in rats, pigeons, and goldfish. *Psychonomic Science,* 1971, *22,* 281–282.

Mackintosh, N. J., Lord, J., & Little, L. Visual and spatial probability learning in pigeons and goldfish. *Psychonomic Science,* 1971, *24,* 221–223.

Margules, D. L., & Olds, J. Identical "feeding" and "rewarding" systems in the lateral hypothalamus of rats. *Science,* 1962, *135,* 374–375.

Marler, P. Behaviour of the chaffinch, *Fringilla coelebs. Behaviour Supplements,* 1956, *5,* 1–184. (a)

Marler, P. Studies of fighting in chaffinches. 3. Proximity as a cause of aggression. *British Journal of Animal Behaviour,* 1956, *4,* 23–30. (b)

Marler, P. *Colobus guereza:* Territoriality and group composition. *Science,* 1969, *163,* 93–95.

Marler, P. Vocalizations of east African monkeys II: Black and white colobus. *Behaviour,* 1972, *42,* 175–197.

Marler, P., & Hamilton, W. J. H., III. *Mechanisms of animal behavior.* New York: Wiley, 1966.

Marshall, A. J. *Bowerbirds: Their displays and breeding cycles.* Oxford: Oxford University Press, 1954.

Mason, W. A., & Green, P. C. The effects of social restriction on the behavior of rhesus monkeys: IV. Responses to a novel environment and to an alien species. *Journal of Comparative and Physiological Psychology,* 1962, *55,* 363–368.

Masure, R. H., & Allee, W. C. Flock organization of the shell parakeet *Melopsittacus undulatus* Shaw. *Ecology,* 1934, *15,* 388–398. (a)

Masure, R. H., & Allee, W. C. The social order in flocks of the common chicken and the pigeon. *Auk,* 1934, *51,* 306–327. (b)

McKinney, C. O. An analysis of zones of intergradation in the side-blotched lizard, *Uta stansburiana* (Sauria: Iguanidae). *Copeia,* 1971, 595–613.

McLaren, I. A. Polygyny as the adaptive function of breeding territory in birds. *Transactions of the Connecticut Academy of Arts and Sciences,* 1972, *44,* 191–210.

McMillan, I. *Man and the California condor.* New York: Dutton, 1968.

Mech, L. D. *The wolf: The ecology and behavior of an endangered species.* Garden City, New York: Natural History Press, 1970.

Menaker, M. Synchronization with the photic environment via extraretinal receptors in the avian brain. In M. Menaker (Ed.), *Biochronometry: Proceedings of a symposium.* Washington: National Academy of Sciences, 1971. Pp. 315–332.

Menaker, M. Nonvisual light reception. *Scientific American,* 1972, *226*(3), 22–29.

Menzel, E. W., Davenport, R. K., & Rogers, C. M. The effects of environmental restriction upon the chimpanzee's responsiveness to objects. *Journal of Comparative and Physiological Psychology,* 1963, *56,* 78–85.

Mills, J. N. Human circadian rhythms. *Physiological Reviews,* 1966, *46,* 128–171.

Miranda, S. B. Visual abilities and pattern preferences of premature infants and full-term neonates. *Journal of Experimental Child Psychology,* 1970, *10,* 189–205.

Mitchell, G. D. Paternalistic behavior in primates. *Psychological Bulletin,* 1969, *71,* 399–417.

Mitchell, G. D., Harlow, H. F., Griffin, D. R., & Møller, C. W. Repeated maternal separation in the monkey. *Psychonomic Science,* 1967, *8,* 197–198.

Miyadi, D. Social life of Japanese monkeys. *Science,* 1954, *143,* 783–786.

Montgomery, K. C. The relation between exploratory behavior and spontaneous alternation in the white rat. *Journal of Comparative and Physiological Psychology,* 1951, *44,* 582–589.

Montgomery, K. C. Exploratory behavior and its relation to spontaneous alternation in a series of maze exposures. *Journal of Comparative and Physiological Psychology,* 1952, *45,* 50–57.

Morgan, C. L. *Animal life and intelligence.* Boston: Ginn, 1891.

Morgan, C. L. *Introduction to comparative psychology.* London: Scott, 1894.

Morgan, C. L. C. Lloyd Morgan. In C. Murchison (Ed.), *History of psychology in autobiography.* Worcester, Massachusetts: Clark University Press, 1932. Pp. 237–264.

Morris, D. The reproductive behaviour of the zebra finch, *Poephila guttata,* with special reference to pseudofemale behaviour and displacement activities. *Behaviour,* 1954, *6,* 271–322.

Morris, D. *The biology of art.* London: Methuen, 1962.

Napier, J. R., & Napier, P. *A handbook of the living primates.* New York: Academic Press, 1967.

Neill, W. T. *The last of the ruling reptiles: Alligators, crocodiles, and their kin.* New York: Columbia University Press, 1971.

Nero, R. W. A behavior study of the redwing blackbird. II. Territoriality. *Wilson Bulletin,* 1956, *68,* 129–150.

Nice, M. M. The role of territoriality in bird life. *American Midland Naturalist,* 1941, *26,* 441–487.

Nice, M. M. Studies in the life history of the song sparrow. II. *Transactions of the Linnaean Society of New York,* 1943, *6,* 1–328.

Noble, C. K. Sexual selection among fishes. *Biological Reviews,* 1938, *13,* 133–158.

Noble, G. K., & Curtis, B. Sexual selection in fishes. *Anatomical Record,* 1935, *64,* Supplement 1, 84.

Oakley, K. P. *Man the tool maker.* (4th ed.) London: British Museum, 1959.

Odum, E. P. The heart rate of small birds. *Science,* 1945, *101,* 153–154.

Olds, J. Pleasure centers in the brain. *Scientific American,* 1956, *195,* 4, 105–116.

Olds, J. Self-stimulation of the brain. *Science,* 1958, *127,* 315–325.

Olds, J., & Milner, P. Positive reinforcement produced by electrical stimulation of septal area and other regions of rat brain. *Journal of Comparative and Physiological Psychology,* 1954, *47,* 419–427.

Orians, G. H. The ecology of blackbird (*Angelaius*) social systems. *Ecological Monographs*, 1961, *31*, 285–312.

Orr, R. T. *Animals in migration.* New York: Macmillan, 1970.

Patterson, I. J. Timing and spacing of broods in the black-headed gull *Larus ridibundus. Ibis*, 1965, *107*, 433–459.

Pavlov, I. P. *Conditioned reflexes.* New York: Dover, 1960. (Originally published: Oxford: Oxford University Press, 1927.)

Pengelley, E. T., & Asmundson, S. M. Free-running periods of endogenous circannian rhythms in the golden-mantled ground squirrel (*Citellus lateralis tescorum*). *Comparative Biochemistry and Physiology*, 1969, *30*, 177–183.

Pengelley, E. T., & Asmundson, S. J. Annual biological clocks. *Scientific American*, 1971, *224*(4), 72–79.

Pengelley, E. T., & Fisher, K. C. Onset and cessation of hibernation under constant temperature and light in the golden-mantled ground squirrel, *Citellus lateralis. Nature*, 1957, *180*, 1371–1372.

Pengelley, E. T., & Fisher, K. C. Rhythmical arousal from hibernation in the golden-mantled ground squirrel, *Citellus lateralis tescorum. Canadian Journal of Zoology*, 1961, *39*, 105–120.

Pengelley, E. T., & Fisher, K. C. The effect of temperature and photoperiod on the yearly hibernating behaviour of captive golden-mantled ground squirrels (*Citellus lateralis tescorum*). *Canadian Journal of Zoology*, 1963, *41*, 1103–1120.

Peterson, R. S., & Bartholomew, G. A. The natural history and behavior of the California sea lion. *Special Publications of the American Society of Mammalogists*, 1967, No. 1.

Petter, J. J. Ecological and behavioural studies of Madagascar lemurs in the field. *Annals of the New York Academy of Sciences*, 1962, *102*, 267–281.

Pfeiffer, J. E. *The emergence of man.* New York: McGraw-Hill, 1969.

Pilbeam, D. *The ascent of man.* New York: Macmillan, 1972.

Poole, T. B. Aggressive play in polecats. *Symposia of the Zoological Society of London*, 1966, *18*, 23–44.

Rand, A. L. Results of the Archbald expeditions, No. 26. Breeding habits of the birds of paradise: *Macgregoria* and *Diphyllodes. American Museum Novitates*, 1940, No. 1073. Pp. 1–14.

Ratner, S. C., & Thompson, R. W. Immobility reactions (fear) of domestic fowl as a function of age and prior experience. *Animal Behaviour*, 1960, *8*, 186–191.

Revusky, S. The role of interference in association over a delay. In W. K. Honig & P. H. R. James (Eds.), *Animal memory.* New York: Academic, 1971. Pp. 155–213.

Revusky, S., & Garcia, J. Learned associations over long delays. In G. H. Bower & J. T. Spence (Eds.), *The psychology of learning and motivation*, Vol. 4. New York: Academic, 1970. Pp. 1–84.

Rheingold, H. L. The effect of a strange environment on the behavior of infants. In B. M. Foss (Ed.), *Determinants of infant behaviour IV.* London: Methuen, 1969. Pp. 137–166.

Romanes, E. *Life and letters of George John Romanes.* (2nd ed.) London: Longmans, Green, 1896.

Romanes, G. J. *Animal intelligence.* London: Kegan Paul and Trench, 1882.

Romanes, G. J. *Mental evolution in animals.* London: Kegan Paul and Trench, 1885.

Romanes, G. J. *Mental evolution in man.* London: Kegan Paul and Trench, 1888.

Rosenblum, L. A., & Cross, H. A. Performance of neonatal monkeys in the visual-cliff situation. *American Journal of Psychology,* 1963, *76,* 318–320.

Rowan, W. Experiments in bird migration, I. Manipulation of the reproductive cycle: Seasonal histological changes in the gonads. *Proceedings of the Boston Society of Natural History,* 1929, *39,* 151–208.

Rowan, W. Light and seasonal reproduction in animals. *Biological Review,* 1938, *13,* 374–402.

Rowell, T. E. Forest living baboons in Uganda. *Journal of Zoology,* London, 1966; *149,* 344–364.

Sackett, G. P. Effects of rearing conditions upon the behavior of rhesus monkeys (*Macaca mulatta*). *Child Development,* 1965, *36,* 855–868.

Salzen, E. A., Imprinting and fear. *Symposia of the Zoological Society of London,* 1962, *8,* 199–217.

Salzen, E. A., & Meyer, C. C. Imprinting: Reversal of a preference established during the critical period. *Nature,* 1967, *215,* 785–786.

Schaffer, H. R., & Emerson, P. E. The development of social attachments in infancy. *Monographs of the Society for Research in Child Development,* 1964, *29*(3), 1–77.

Schaller, G. B. *The mountain gorilla.* Chicago: University of Chicago Press, 1963.

Schaller, G. B., & Emlen, J. T., Jr. The ontogeny of avoidance behavior in some precocial birds. *Animal Behaviour,* 1961, *10,* 370–381.

Schenkel, R. Play, exploration, and territoriality in the wild lion. *Symposia of the Zoological Society of London,* 1966, *18,* 11–22.

Schiff, W. The perception of impending collision: A study of visually directed avoidant behavior. *Psychological Monographs,* 1965, *79*(604), 1–26.

Schjelderup-Ebbe, T. Social behavior of birds. In C. Murchison (Ed.), *A handbook of social psychology.* Worcester, Massachusetts: Clark University Press, 1935. Pp. 947–972.

Schwab, R. G. Circannian testicular periodicity in the European starling in the absence of photoperiodic change. In M. Menaker (Ed.), *Biochronometry: Proceedings of a symposium.* Washington: National Academy of Sciences, 1971. Pp. 428–447.

Schwassmann, H. O. Biological rhythms. In W. S. Hoar & D. S. Randall (Eds.), *Fish physiology*, Vol. 6. New York: Academic Press, 1971.

Scott, J. P. The social behavior of dogs and wolves: An illustration of sociobiological systematics. *Annals of the New York Academy of Sciences*, 1950, *51*, 1009–1021.

Scott, J. P. *Early experience and the organization of behavior.* Belmont, California: Brooks/Cole, 1968.

Scott, J. P., & Fuller, J. L. *Genetics of the social behavior of the dog.* Chicago: University of Chicago Press, 1965.

Scott, J. P., & Marston, M. V. Critical periods affecting the development of normal and mal-adjustive social behavior in puppies. *Journal of Genetic Psychology*, 1950, *77*, 25–60.

Sechenov, I. M. Reflexes of the brain. Originally published in 1863. In K. Koshtoyants (Ed.), *I. M. Sechenov: Selected physiological and psychological works.* Moscow: Foreign Language Publishing House, not dated. Pp. 31–139.

Seligman, M. E. P. On the generality of the laws of learning. *Psychological Review*, 1970, *77*, 406–418.

Shaw, E. The schooling of fishes. *Scientific American*, 1962, *206*(6), 128–138.

Sheffield, F. D. A drive-induction theory of reinforcement. In R. N. Haber (Ed.), *Current research in motivation.* New York: Holt, Rinehart and Winston, 1966. Pp. 98–111. (Originally distributed in mimeographed form, 1954.)

Shettleworth, S. J. Constraints on learning. In D. S. Lehrman, R. A. Hinde, & E. Shaw (Eds.), *Advances in the study of behavior*, 4. New York: Academic, 1972, Pp. 1–68.

Simons, E. L. *Primate evolution.* New York: Macmillan, 1972.

Simons, E. L., Pilbeam, D., & Ettel, P. C. Controversial taxonomy of fossil hominids. *Science*, 1969, *166*, 258–259.

Skinner, B. F. *The behavior of organisms.* New York: Appleton-Century-Crofts, 1938.

Skinner, B. F. Are theories of learning necessary? *Psychological Review*, 1950, *57*, 193–216.

Skinner, B. F. *Science and human nature.* New York: Macmillan, 1953.

Skinner, B. F. A case history in the scientific method. *American Psychologist*, 1956, *11*, 221–233.

Skinner, B. F. The experimental analysis of behavior. *American Scientist*, 1957, *45*, 343–371.

Skinner, B. F. The phylogeny and ontogeny of behavior. *Science*, 1966, *153*, 1205–1213.

Skinner, B. F. The phylogeny and ontogeny of behavior. In B. F. Skinner, *Contingencies by reinforcement: A theoretical analysis.* New York: Appleton-Century-Crofts, 1969. Pp. 172–217.

Sluckin, W. *Imprinting and early learning.* Chicago: Aldine, 1965.

Sluckin, W. *Early learning in man and animal.* London: Allen and Unwin, 1970.

Smith, C. C. The adaptive nature of social organization in the genus of tree squirrels *Tamiasciurus. Ecological Monographs,* 1968, *38,* 31–63.

Sokolov, E. N. *Vospriiate i uslovny refleks.* Moscow: University of Moscow Press, 1958. (Available in translation in *Perception and the conditioned reflex.* New York and London: Pergamon Press, 1964.)

Sokolov, E. N. Neuronal models and the orienting reflex. In M. A. Brazier (Ed.), *Central nervous system and behavior.* New York: Josiah Macy, Jr. Foundation, 1960. Pp. 187–276.

Spaulding, D. A. Instinct: With original observations of young animals. *Macmillan's Magazine,* 1873, *27,* 282–293.

Spencer-Booth, Y. The behaviour of group companions towards rhesus monkey infants. *Animal Behaviour,* 1968, *16,* 541– 557.

Spencer-Booth, Y., & Hinde, R. A. Effects of separating rhesus monkey infants from their mothers for six days. *Journal of Child Psychology and Psychiatry,* 1967, *7,* 179–197.

Spencer-Booth, Y., & Hinde, R. A. Individual differences in the responses of rhesus monkeys to a period of separation from their mothers. *Journal of Child Psychology and Psychiatry,* 1970, *11,* 159–176.

Spitz, R. A. Hospitalism: An inquiry into the genesis of psychiatric conditions in early childhood. *Psychoanalytic Study of the Child,* 1945, *1,* 53–74.

Spitz, R. A. Hospitalism: A follow-up report on investigation described in Volume 1, 1945. *Psychoanalytic Study of the Child,* 1946, *2,* 113–117.

Spitz, R. A., & Wolf, K. M. Anaclitic depression: An inquiry into the genesis of psychiatric conditions in early childhood. *Psychoanalytic Study of the Child,* 1945, *1,* 313–342.

Squier, L. H. Reversal learning improvement in the fish *Astronotus ocellatus* (Oscar). *Psychonomic Science,* 1969, *14,* 143–144.

Stebbins, R. C. Activity changes in the striped plateau lizard with evidence on influence of the parietal eye. *Copeia,* 1963, 681–690.

Struthsaker, T. T. Social behaviour of mother and infant vervet monkeys (*Cercopithecus aethiops*). *Animal Behaviour,* 1971, *19,* 233–250.

Sutcliffe, A. J. Spotted hyaena: Crusher, gnawer, and collector of bones. *Nature,* 1970, *227,* 1110–1113.

Teleki, G. The omnivorous chimpanzee. *Scientific American,* 1973, *228,* 32–42.

Thorndike, E. L. Animal intelligence: An experimental study of associative processes in animals. *Psychological Monograph Review Supplements,* 1898, *2*(4, Whole No. 8). Pp. 1–109.

Thorndike, E. L. A note on the psychology of fishes. *American Naturalist,* 1899, *33,* 923–926.

Thorndike, E. L. The mental life of monkeys. *Psychological Review Monograph Supplements,* 1901, *15,* 1–57.

Thorndike, E. L. *Educational psychology.* New York: Lemcke & Buechner, 1904.

Thorndike, E. L. *Animal intelligence.* New York: Macmillan, 1911.

Thorndike, E. L. Edward Lee Thorndike. In C. Murchison (Ed.), *A history of psychology in autobiography,* Vol. III. Worcester, Massachusetts: Clark University Press, 1936. Pp. 263–270.

Thorpe, W. H. The learning of song patterns by birds, with especial reference to the song of the chaffinch *Fringilla coelebs. Ibis,* 1958, *100,* 535–557.

Thorpe, W. H. *Bird song: The biology of vocal communication and expression in birds.* Cambridge: Cambridge University Press, 1961.

Tinbergen, L. The natural control of insects. I. Factors influencing the intensity of predation by songbirds. *Archives Neerlandaises de Zoologie,* 1960, *31,* 259–379.

Tinbergen, N. *The study of instinct.* Oxford: Oxford University Press, 1951.

Tinbergen, N. The curious behavior of the stickleback. *Scientific American,* 1952, *187*(6), 22–26.

Tinbergen, N. *The herring gull's world.* London: Collins, 1953.

Tinbergen, N. On aims and methods of ethology. *Zeitschrift für Tierpsychologie,* 1963, *20,* 410–429.

Tobias, P. V. The Olduvai Bed I hominine with special reference to its cranial capacity. *Nature,* 1964, *202,* 3–4.

Tobias, P. V. The cranium and maxillary dentition of *Australopithecus (Zinjanthropus) boisei.* In L. S. B. Leakey (Ed.), *Olduvai Gorge,* Vol. 2. Cambridge: Cambridge University Press, 1967.

Tobias, P. V. *The brain in hominid evolution.* New York: Columbia University Press, 1971.

Van Lawick-Goodall, J. The behaviour of free-living chimpanzees in the Gombe Stream Reserve. *Animal Behaviour Monographs,* 1968, *1,* 165–311.

Van Lawick-Goodall, J. *In the shadow of man.* London: Collins, 1971.

Walker, B. W. Periodicity of spawning of the grunion, *Leuresthes teunis.* Doctoral dissertation, University of California at Los Angeles, 1949.

Walker, B. W. A guide to the grunion. *California Fish and Game,* 1952, 409–420.

Warden, C. J. The historical development of comparative psychology. *Psychological Review,* 1927, *34,* 57–85, 135–168.

Washburn, S. L., & DeVore, I. Social behavior of baboons and early man. In S. L. Washburn (Ed.), *Social life of early man.* New York: Wenner-Gren Foundation, 1961. Pp. 91–105. (a)

Washburn, S. L., & DeVore, I. The social life of baboons. *Scientific American,* 1961, *204*(6), 62–71. (b)

Watson, J. B. Psychology as the behaviorist views it. *Psychological Review,* 1913, *20,* 158–177.

Watson, J. B. *Introduction to comparative psychology.* New York: Holt, 1914. (a)

Watson, J. B. *Psychology from the standpoint of a behaviorist.* Philadelphia: Lippincott, 1914. (b)

Watson, J. B. John Broadus Watson. In Carl Murchison (Ed.), *History of psychology in autobiography,* Vol. 3. Worcester, Massachusetts: Clark University Press, 1936. Pp. 271–281.

Welsh, D. Breeding and territoriality of the palm warbler in a Nova Scotia bog. *Canadian Field-Naturalist,* 1971, *85,* 31–37.

Welty, J. C. *The life of birds.* Philadelphia: Saunders, 1962.

Whitman, C. O. Animal behavior. *Biological lectures from the Marine Biological Laboratory of Woods Hole, 1898.* Boston: Woods Hole Biological Laboratory, 1899. Pp. 285–338.

Wickler, W. *Mimicry in plants and animals.* New York: McGraw-Hill, 1968.

Wiewandt, T. A. Vocalization, aggressive behavior, and territoriality in the bullfrog, *Rana catesbeiana. Copeia,* 1969, 276–285.

Wikler, A. Pharmacological dissociation of behavior and EEG sleep patterns in dogs: Morphine, N-allylnormorphine, and atropine. *Proceedings of the Society for Experimental Biology and Medicine,* 1952, *79,* 261–265.

Williams, C. D., & Kuchta, J. C. Exploratory behavior in two mazes with dissimilar alternatives. *Journal of Comparative and Physiological Psychology,* 1957, *50,* 509–513.

Winn, H. E. Comparative reproductive behavior and ecology of fourteen species of darters (*Pisces percidae*). *Ecological Monographs,* 1958, *28,* 155–191.

Wolfson, A. Regulation of annual periodicity in the migration and reproduction of birds. *Cold Spring Harbor Symposia on Quantitative Biology. 25. Biological clocks.* Cold Spring Harbor, Long Island: Long Island Biological Association, 1960, 507–514.

Yakovlev, P. I. Bechterev. In M. A. Brazier (Ed.), *The central nervous system and behavior.* New York: Josiah Macy, Jr. Foundation, 1959. Pp. 187–210.

Zimbardo, P. G., & Miller, N. E. Facilitation of exploration by hunger in rats. *Journal of Comparative and Physiological Psychology,* 1958, *51,* 43–46.

INDEX

Acheson, N. H., 140
Acoustic insects, courtship displays of, 109
Action-specific energy, 41, 43
Adaptation, 106–112
Adaptive correlation, 110
African mouthbrooder, 29, 131–132
Aggregation, 102–106
Ainsworth, M. D., 127–128
Alarm stimuli, 75
Alaska fur seal, 132
Allee, W. C., 103, 104–105
Alligator, 131
Altruistic behavior, 110–111
Amphibians:
 circannual rhythms in, 87
 pairing in, 133
Animal hypnosis, 72
Anonymous group, 102–103
Antelope, kob, 101
Anthropoidea, 135–138
Antisocial responses, 90, 93
Appell, G., 129
Appetites, 34–36
Appetitive behavior, 37–38, 41
Archbold's bowerbird, 97
Arena, 96, 108–109
Aristotle, 2
Armstrong, E. A., 96
Arousal, 64, 71
Arrival distance, 100
Art, 160, 163
Aschoff, J., 80, 83
Aschoff's rule, 83
Asmundson, S. J., 87–88
Association, 8, 14, 16, 20
Atlantic salmon, 97
Attachment. *See* Socialization
"Aunts," 122, 132
Australopithecus, 146–147, 154–156, 161
 africanus, 147–150, 152
 boisei, 149, 152–154, 155
 robustus, 149, 152–154
Aversion, 34–36
Avoidance learning, 49, 52–53, 55–56, 76–77

Baboon:
 gelada, 141–142
 hamadryas, 141–142
 sacred, 141–142
 savannah, 140–141, 144
Baerends, G. P., 131
Baerends-van Roon, J. M., 131

Baeumer, E., 75
Barnes, G. W., 67
Bartholomew, G. A., 96–97, 109, 132
Bates, H. W., 76
Batesian mimicry, 76
Bateson, P. P. G., 116, 118
Begging peck, 48–51
Behavioral synchrony, 105–106, 111–112
Behaviorism, rise of, 22–23
Behrensmeyer, A. K., 156
Bekhterev, V. M., 13–14, 25, 59
Berlyne, D. E., 63–64
Bird of paradise, 97
Birds:
 pairing in, 133
 predation in, 76
Birdsong, 53–54
Bitterman, M. E., 29–32
Black, D. R., 158
Black, F. A., 133
Black and white colobus monkey, 140
Blackbird, redwing, 95
Black grouse, 108–110
Black-headed gull, 101, 111–112
Black-tailed prairie dog, 99
Blest, A. D., 77
Blue jay, 32
Bolles, R. C., 52–53, 71
Bonnet macaque, 123
Boring, E. G., 16, 20
Bouissou, M.-F., 103–104
Bowerbirds, 97, 98
Bowlby, J., 124, 129
Brachiation, 138
Brain, C. K., 153
Brain stimulation, 57–58
Breland, K., 51–52
Breland, M., 51–52
Brodbeck, A. J., 122
Broom, R., 153
Brower, J. V., 49, 76
Brower, L. P., 49, 76
Brown, J. L., 99, 105
Bryan, J. E., 46
Bufo bufo, 38
Bunting, yellow, 77
Burns, P. E., 153
Bushbaby, Demidoff's, 138–139
Butler, R. A., 61, 69
Butterfield, P. A., 133
Butterflies, 76, 77

California condor, 79
California sea lion, 96, 109

185